LASER APPLICATIONS

Volume 4

CONTRIBUTORS

ROBERT K. ERF

A. KORPEL

GARY K. STARKWEATHER

LASER APPLICATIONS

Edited by

JOSEPH W. GOODMAN

Department of Electrical Engineering
Stanford University
Stanford, California

MONTE ROSS

McDonnell Douglas Astronautics Company
St. Louis, Missouri

VOLUME 4

ACADEMIC PRESS   1980

A Subsidiary of Harcourt Brace Jovanovich, Publishers

New York London Toronto Sydney San Francisco

ACADEMIC PRESS, INC.
111 Fifth Avenue, New York, New York 10003

United Kingdom Edition published by
ACADEMIC PRESS, INC. (LONDON) LTD.
24/28 Oval Road, London NW1 7DX

LIBRARY OF CONGRESS CATALOG CARD NUMBER: 79–154380

ISBN 0–12–431904–1

PRINTED IN THE UNITED STATES OF AMERICA

80 81 82 83   9 8 7 6 5 4 3 2 1

CONTENTS

Application of Laser Speckle to Measurement

ROBERT K. ERF

Laser Applications: Video Disc

A. KORPEL

High-Speed Laser Printing Systems

GARY K. STARKWEATHER

LIST OF CONTRIBUTORS

Numbers in parentheses indicate the pages on which the authors' contributions begin.

ROBERT K. ERF, United Technologies Research Center, East Hartford, Connecticut 06108 (1)

A. KORPEL,* Zenith Radio Corporation, Chicago, Illinois 60639 (71)

GARY K. STARKWEATHER, Xerox Corporation, Palo Alto Research Center, Palo Alto, California 94304 (125)

* Present address: Division of Information Engineering, The University of Iowa, Iowa City, Iowa 52242.

PREFACE

In this fourth volume of *Laser Applications,* three topics are covered, each representing an application of lasers that has reached a high state of refinement. The articles appearing in this volume are written by individuals who have played important roles in these developments, and who speak from first-hand knowledge of the engineering problems encountered in bringing a new technology to the point of useful application.

In the first article, Robert K. Erf describes the applications of laser speckle to problems of measurement. Since their first observation in the early 1960s, the random interference patterns known as speckle have generally been regarded as nuisances. Speckle reduces the effective resolution of coherent imaging systems, whether these systems use optical, acoustical, or microwave radiation. However, speckle has its redeeming features. In particular, as described in this article, it has been usefully applied to a considerable variety of engineering measurement problems.

The second subject discussed is optical video discs, for which the laser plays an important role in both the recording of master discs and the reading of information from mass-produced copies. The author, A. Korpel, served as Director of Research in Technical Physics at Zenith Corporation during a time period when that company was heavily involved in research on video discs. The development of video-disc technology has been a truly international enterprise, with major efforts in the Netherlands, France, Japan, and the United States. The first commercial optical video-disc players for home entertainment were introduced on a limited basis in December of 1978 through a joint effort of Magnavox and Philips corporations, and further penetration of the commercial marketplace is taking place slowly but surely. This tech-

nology undoubtedly has a bright future, not only in the home entertainment field, but also in the area of digital data storage.

The third and last article in this volume describes the technology
and engineering problems associated with high-speed laser printing
systems. The author, Gary Starkweather, played a central role in the
development of the Xerox 9700 copier, which is one of three such
systems available today from different manufacturers. Of the various
applications described in this volume, high-speed laser printing has
achieved the greatest commercial success at this time. A major reason
for this success must surely be the relative ease with which light beams
can be directed and redirected to particular positions in space.

The Editors hope that this collection of articles will prove helpful
to practicing optical engineers who regard the laser as an important
tool for the solution of a wide variety of practical problems. Technical
progress depends heavily on experience, and we trust that this oppor-
tunity to share the experience of others will benefit the reader in his
or her future applications of laser technology.

Monte Ross wishes to acknowledge the diligence of his co-editor,
Joseph W. Goodman, whose perseverance has resulted in the fine set
of articles, which constitute Volume 4.

CONTENTS OF PREVIOUS VOLUMES

LASER APPLICATIONS

Volume 4

APPLICATION OF LASER SPECKLE TO MEASUREMENT

Robert K. Erf

United Technologies Research Center
East Hartford, Connecticut

1

I. Introduction

In an earlier work (Erf, 1974) the present author introduced the subject of holographic nondestructive testing by suggesting that perhaps it emerged just in time to "save" holography, for at last there was a real application for this visual fantasia. In a later book (Erf, 1978), a brief citation from Stetson's (1975) excellent speckle review paper carried this air of facetiousness several steps further by questioning whether the most practical contribution of holography was to call our attention to laser speckle, for indeed, this phenomenon was most annoying to the serious holographers. Such frivolity is intended simply to indicate that, indeed, it was the intensive study of speckle reduction, a subject undertaken to improve the holographic process and reviewed in detail by McKechnie (1975) in Dainty's (1975) book on "Laser Speckle" that "ignited" the development of speckle metrology.

It should be noted at the outset that the intent of the present article is to review this new technology for performing high-sensitivity measurement from a practical orientation. To this end, experimental methods and applications of speckle metrology will be introduced and described with sufficient illustrative examples to demonstrate its potential. For additional information and more mathematical detail, the previously referenced, edited works "Speckle Metrology" (Erf, 1978) and "Laser Speckle and Related Phenomena" (Dainty, 1975), along with Vest's authored work entitled "Holographic Interferometry" (Vest, 1979), are recommended to the reader. The first, to which considerable reference will be made, along with entries to the original publications, by definition is oriented toward measurement techniques, while the latter two contain contributions on speckle interferometry.

To properly set the stage for discussing the experimental methodology of speckle measurement, the physical properties of speckle are briefly considered in Section II, along with references to detailed accounts of speckle statistics and speckle correlation. With proper mathematical formulation and accompanying verbal description, a precise definition of speckle is possible. However, a visual expression of the phenomenon is far more graphic than words and equations. To this end, Karl Stetson's speckle photographic creation, entitled "Fringe Nebula," is presented as Fig. 1. Artistically fashioned therein is a background of speckle, illustrating the characteristic pattern familiar to anyone who has observed a laser-illuminated scene, overlaid in one area with a "Young's fringe pattern," typical of those obtained during

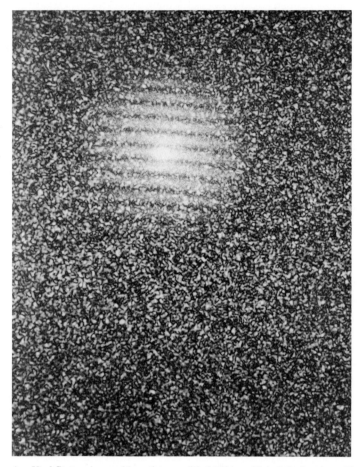

FIG. 1. Karl Stetson's speckle artistry entitled "Fringe Nebula" showing a Young's fringe pattern on a background of speckle.

analysis of a laser specklegram. This particular technique of fringe formation in a diffraction halo is one of the most widely used methods of reducing data from double-exposure laser recordings.

It is perhaps appropriate to note at this point that the fringe characteristics, such as sharpness and contrast, seen in Fig. 1 and depicted throughout the chapter, may not seem as aesthetically pleasing as those obtained by holographic interferometry. (This is especially apparent in the television implementation of speckle metrology to be described later in the article.) However, the greater simplicity of the method, together with the versatility afforded in data reduction, suggests a competitiveness which cannot be ignored in developing optical metrological procedures. For example, fringes of the type depicted in Fig. 1, whose spacing and angular orientation can be quantitatively related to the amount and direction of object displacement, are formed quite simply upon laser interrogation of the specklegram. This form of data reduction is considered in depth in Section III of the present article, along with other analysis procedures (especially full-image reconstruction) and the experimental methods of speckle photography and various types of speckle interferometry for recording specklegrams. Utilization of the fringe data so obtained to measure displacement and strain is one subject of Section IV, which covers several metrological applications of speckle. Additional subjects to be discussed therein include surface roughness measurement, vibration and deformation analysis, velocity measurement, nondestructive inspection, and contouring.

Of further interest is the fact that speckle is one of the easiest of the many popularized laser characteristics (such as high peak powers, monochromaticity, coherence length, and collimation) to take advantage of; for, in the simplest case, as described in Section III, only a camera is required along with the laser to record the specklegram. In addition, the compatibility of speckle techniques with video processing has been developed and used extensively for vibration modal analysis as well as many of the other areas cited earlier. This technology, now commonly referred to as electronic speckle pattern interferometry, or ESPI, offers the advantage of sophisticated electronic processing, coupled with TV display and videotape storage. In-depth consideration of this topic, including the equipment, techniques, and examples of application, is the subject of Section V.

The plethora of possibilities, both in application and execution, indicated here seems to suggest a panacea for problems encountered in optical metrology. It is not surprising, therefore, that speckle, like most technological tools, both old and new, does have its limitations and these are pointed out in Section VI, along with some general considerations relevant to speckle implementation, and comparisons among the various speckle techniques and with holographic interferometry.

As a further introduction to the present chapter, a brief, generalized discussion of speckle terminology is warranted, for as the reader will learn upon delving into the referenced material, there is an abundance of definitions for similar processes. This, of course, is not uncommon in emerging technologies, and the purpose of the following is simply to alert the reader to potential dualities of meaning. Albeit, there is a wide variety of experimental arrangements, as we shall learn in Section III, all of the metrological applications of speckle can be categorized as either speckle photography or speckle interferometry. As an example of the proliferation of terms, the former is often referred to as direct laser photography, and some prefer to think of some versions of the latter as in-line, or on-axis, image plane holography, for the similarity of the setups is clear. Further, some experimenters think of all the techniques as speckle interferometry, and indeed, the verbal distinction is quite subtle. Consider, for instance, that both speckle photography and speckle interferometry involve photography (or other appropriate means of visualization) and, since speckle itself is the result of a self-interference between the coherent wavelets reflected from an optically "rough" surface, both obviously involve interferometry. In addition, utilization of either method generally involves examination of the result in such a way as to yield fringes indicative of object motion. However, in a practical sense, it is the arrangement of the experimental components themselves which generally best defines the process. More importantly, the selection of a method, by whatever name, appropriate to a specific task is the prime consideration, and that is the intent of the following sections.

II. Speckle Properties

Although the phenomenon of speckle is most often associated with the "twinkling" appearance of an object illuminated with a laser, the history of speckle, or speckle-like phenomenon, predates the invention of the laser in the early 1960s by well over 100 years. Not surprisingly, such great names as Newton and Lord Rayleigh, along with others, have been associated with the phenomenon of speckle as related by Dainty (1975) and Goodman (1975). However, the intended purpose of the present discussion is to deal with modern-day applications of the speckle process, with the emphasis on actual engineering measurement problems. In that context, our interest is in the granular appearance; a random distribution of light and dark speckles as seen in the background of Fig. 1, that diffusely reflecting and transmitting surfaces "take-on" when viewed or photographed under laser illumination. This "optical noise" can be quite bothersome because of its deleterious effect on image quality. However, the light contributing to the formation of each individual speckle is fully coherent,[1] and thus speckle is, in effect, a self-interference phenomenon between waves coming from different elementary areas of a rough surface. In our sense, rough refers to random height variations on the order of a wavelength of the light being used and greater. Thus, all but the quite highly polished optical surfaces are candidates for the speckle metrological studies to be discussed herein. Indeed, the phenomenon has been successfully applied to the measurement of surface roughness itself.

A complete treatise on the properties of speckle would include consideration of the statistics of laser speckle patterns and discussions of speckle correlation and related topics. Since the specific details of these subjects are generally not necessary for an experimental understanding of speckle applications to measurement problems, they are felt to be somewhat outside the intended scope of the present coverage, and the reader is referred elsewhere for detailed treatments. Although the possible sources are numerous, Goodman (1975) and Burch (1970) have both dealt extensively with speckle statistics and other topics, while several contributors to "Speckle Metrology" including Stetson (1978a) and Asakura (1978), have given consideration to correlation, and just as important, decorrelation of speckle patterns as it limits application of the methods.

One metrological field somewhat closely tied to the statistics, contrast, and correlation of speckle patterns is that of surface roughness measurement alluded to just earlier. A comprehensive review article on this subject, including the necessary mathematical treatment along with extensive referencing, has been prepared by Asakura (1978). Only a summary of the capabilities of speckle in this area will be provided in Section IV on applications.

However, before proceeding to the speckle techniques themselves, and thence the applications, there is one important property deserving of comment in this abbreviated presentation: speckle size, a statistical

---

[1] Although not reported in the literature of that day, Ennos had verified the coherent nature of laser speckle in a 1966 experiment (Ennos, 1975) using an optical arrangement not unlike the reference wave speckle interferometers of today. Laser speckles have a measurable intensity and definite phases which are different from, and relatable to, each other. Thus, a few years later, in 1969 [later published (Leendertz, 1970a)], Leendertz reported on the ability to interfere two speckle fields themselves producing a third speckle pattern whose characteristics were dependent upon the relative phase of the original fields.

average of the distance between adjacent regions of maximum and minimum brightness. The importance of speckle size to the user-oriented applications engineer lies in its direct relationship to the geometry and dimensions of the experimental optical system parameters, and its role in establishing limitations on the speckle measurement range. For example, the measurement of in-plane translation can be effected by a double-exposure (one before and one after the object movement) recording of a laser-illuminated object. However, the technique requires the complete separation of the corresponding speckles within the two recorded speckle patterns; thus, the individual speckle size sets the lower measurable limit in such a study.

The speckle size d_{sp} is inversely proportional to the limiting aperture in the optical system and, in terms of the experimental system parameters employed, can be expressed as shown in Fig. 2. In the objective speckle case of Fig. 2a, the size of the limiting aperture is established by the diameter of the laser illumination beam itself. Certainly of more practical interest are those cases involving optical imaging of the diffuse object surface, or subjective speckle, using a lens of focal length f and diameter d_ℓ as illustrated in Figs. 2b and 2c. The latter represents the

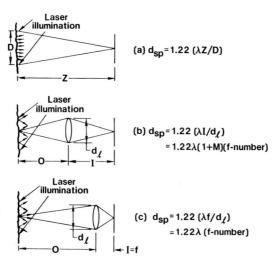

FIG. 2. Parameters and formulation to determine speckle size for: (a) objective case; (b) general subjective case; and (c) subjective case with object at infinity.

limiting case of an object at infinity, or a large distance from the lens
($O \ggg f$). In these cases, the diameter of the lens, or the f-number in
the limiting case, is the controlling factor. It is also convenient to think
of the more general case (Fig. 2b) in terms of the f-number and magnification M of the optical system. Using the standard lens formulation,
the image distance I is equivalent to the lens focal length f multiplied
by $(1 + M)$. Then, substitution of the f-number for f/d_e provides the
second expression shown in Fig. 2b. A similiar substitution (f-number
$= f/d_e$) also provides the second expression of Fig. 2c. Using the direct
proportionality to the f-number, as in Fig. 2c, typical speckle sizes for
He–Ne laser illumination can be seen to vary from 1 to 12 μm as the
lens is stopped down from $f/1.4$ to $f/16$. A convenient working aperture
is $f/4$, inferring a speckle size of ∼3 μm for this case, or ∼6 μm for
the case of one-to-one imaging, i.e., a magnification $M = 1$.

III. Experimental Methods

We have noted the size properties of speckle relative to metrological
applications and now turn our attention to the experimental procedures
themselves. We shall cover the basic techniques of speckle photography and interferometry in their various forms, along with the data
reduction procedures associated with each. Individual discussions of
speckle-shearing interferometry and white light speckle will then be
presented, and throughout the chapter, appropriate specific examples
will be included to illustrate typical areas of application. General com-
ments on lasers, film, stability requirements, and other topics common
to the different speckle recording techniques will be deferred to the
concluding section of the article.

A. SPECKLE PHOTOGRAPHY

Perhaps in its simplest form speckle photography involves the
straightforward double-exposure recording of a laser-illuminated object
in two different positions or states of stress. Probing of the processed
film recording (transparency) with an unexpanded laser beam produces
a set of fringes, whose spacing is inversely proportional to the in-plane
surface displacement, and whose angular orientation is perpendicular
to the direction of displacement. The fringes, "embedded" in a dif-

fraction halo, are produced as a result of a slight, but uniform displacement of the speckle pattern present on the object between the two exposures; a process reminiscent of, and based upon the principle involved in, Thomas Young's demonstration of the interference of light emerging from a dual pinhole arrangement. The preceding three-sentence description of the entire process (data gathering and reduction) of speckle photography serves to illustrate its basic simplicity, but some experimental detail will aid in our understanding.

To illustrate schematically the technique, consider the diagram of Fig. 3, taken after Hung (1978) (original citations: Archbold *et al.*, 1970; Duffy, 1974). As can be seen, all that is required in addition to a beam of coherent illumination and the object itself, is a camera. The method is perhaps best understood by describing its application to the measurement of in-plane displacement. The object is imaged on the film plane of the camera, and a double-exposure photograph is recorded with one exposure made before translation, and the other after. Since the relative phase of the reflected illumination forming the speckled image in each exposure is unchanged, the photograph contains two identical speckle patterns separated by an amount equal to the object displacement multiplied by the magnification of the optical system. (It is assumed that the displacement is greater than the speckle size, as discussed in Section II.) Thus direct microscopic examination of a print of the processed film would yield the desired displacement information.

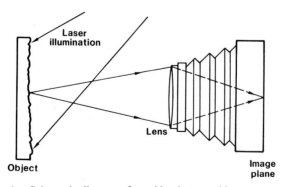

FIG. 3. Schematic diagram of speckle photographic arrangement.

1. *Young's Fringe Analysis of Speckle Photographs*

On the other hand, if one uses direct illumination of the processed film transparency with an unexpanded laser beam (Fig. 4), one can project the Young's fringe pattern, alluded to earlier, from which the displacement can be calculated. (A typical Young's fringe pattern generated by this method is presented in Fig. 5.)

The mathematics of this case are straightforward since the translation T of the object is simply the distance d_S between speckles on the recording divided by the magnification M of the speckle recording optical system,

$$T = \frac{d_S}{M} \tag{1}$$

The classical Young's fringes are oriented perpendicular to a line joining the slits and separated by a distance d_F that is directly proportional to the distance D between the plane containing the slits (the speckle transparency in Fig. 4 of our analogy) and the observation screen and inversely proportional to the slit spacing, or distance d_S between the speckles in our analogy,

$$d_F = \frac{\lambda D}{d_S} \tag{2}$$

where λ is the laser source wavelength. Thus, by combining Eqs. (1)

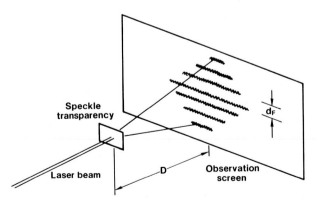

Speckle transparency

d_F

Laser beam

D

Observation screen

Fig. 4.   Schematic diagram of Young's fringe formation with unexpanded laser beam for specklegram analysis.

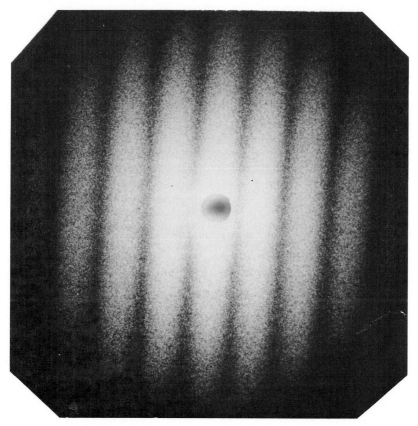

FIG. 5. A typical Young's fringe pattern embedded in a diffraction halo. (Displacement is inversely proportional to fringe spacing, and in a direction perpendicular to the fringes.)

and (2), the in-plane translation of the object at the point of interrogation can be expressed as

$$T = \frac{\lambda D}{M d_F}$$ (3)

which can be utilized to determine the direction (perpendicular to the fringes) and degree (magnitude) of the in-plane displacement at any point on the object by probing a transparency of the speckle photograph with an unexpanded laser beam at the point of interest.

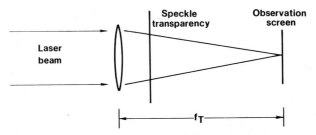

FIG. 6. Alternate scheme of processing specklegram for the formation of Young's fringes in back focal plane of lens.

Similarly, if the entire object is translated uniformly, illumination of the film in a converging wavefront, as illustrated in Fig. 6, will produce a Young's fringe pattern, from which the translation or displacement may be measured using

$$T = \frac{\lambda f_T}{M d_F} \qquad (4)$$

again, with the direction of displacement perpendicular to the fringes.

2. *Full-Image Analysis of Speckle Photographs*

An alternative approach to the analysis of speckle photographs permits a full-image reconstruction of the object covered with fringes, providing a picture more reminiscent of holographic interferometry, and generally more familiar to the casual reader than the Young's fringe pattern methodology just described. Data reduction is performed by a Fourier filtering process as shown schematically in Fig. 7, producing fringe patterns representing contours of constant displacement such as those depicted in Fig. 8, which illustrates the in-plane displacements of a cantilever beam loaded at its free end, for six different filtering positions. These results were taken from Hung, who prefers to think of speckle photography as single-beam speckle interferometry, and explains the phenomenon using an interferometric theory and a moiré effect (Hung, 1978).

With reference to Fig. 7, a transparency of the double-exposed and processed speckle photograph is placed in the input plane and a filtering aperture in the Fourier filtering plane. The position of that aperture can be varied in both azimuth and radial distance from the optical axis (η and q in Fig. 7). The former determines the direction in which the object displacement is resolved, and the latter the density of the contours, or sensitivity of the measurement. Thus, by filtering in the vertical direction (placing the aperture along the vertical axis) with an ever-increasing q, the displacement vector for vertical surface motion is obtained with an increasing sensitivity as can be seen in Fig. 8. Likewise the displacement vector sensitivity to horizontal motion is obtained by filtering in the horizontal direction. Indeed, the displacement in any direction can be determined by varying the azimuthal angle η at which the aperture is located. The incremental displacement ΔT of the object between two adjacent fringes in the spatially filtered image is, in the parameters of Fig. 7 (Hung, 1978),

$$\Delta T = \frac{\lambda H}{qM} \tag{5}$$

where M is the magnification employed in recording the original speckle photograph, H the distance between the speckle transparency and the filtering plane, q the radial distance of the aperture from the optical axis, and λ the filtering wavelength. Similarly, the total displacement T at a given point in the image can then be expressed as

$$T = \frac{N\lambda H}{qM}, \qquad N = 0, \pm 1, \pm 2 \ldots \tag{6}$$

Thus, to determine, for example, the vertical displacement at the midpoint of the free end of the cantilevered beam in Fig. 8, the fringe order is established by counting the fringes out to the point of interest (~ 6, 9, or 12 from the bottom to the top reconstructions of Fig. 8) and multiplying the result by the ΔT of Eq. (5) for the particular aperture

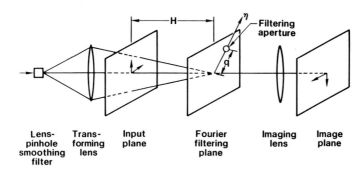

FIG. 7. Fourier filtering arrangement for a full-image reconstruction of the object.

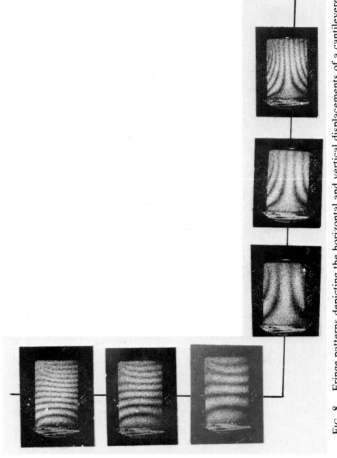

FIG. 8. Fringe patterns depicting the horizontal and vertical displacements of a cantilevered beam obtained from the various filtering positions in the Fourier filtering plane of Fig. 7. From Hung (1978).

position selected along the vertical or Y axis. Similiarly, the horizontal vector displacement for the same point is seen to be zero in any of the three reconstructions obtained by filtering in the horizontal direction (along the X axis). A calibration procedure described by Cloud (1975) can be used to obviate the need for accurate measurement of the various parameters. It involves performing a speckle analysis of a calibrated specimen, exhibiting a range of known displacements, in the same optical setup (physical dimensions, aperture position, and magnification) that is used for the test object.

A practical experimental arrangement for performing the full-image analysis is illustrated in Fig. 9, where the spatial filtering is performed by the camera lens aperture (Stetson, 1975). The camera and transparency of the speckle photograph are fixed in position such that the latter is imaged onto the film plane of the former. This rigid assembly is arranged to rotate about the center of the photographic transparency in two orthogonal directions thereby translating the camera aperture relative to the focal point of the transforming lens L and permitting selection of the filtering aperture location.

3. *Measurement Sensitivity of Speckle Photography*

A powerful attribute of speckle metrological technology is apparent in Eqs. (3) and (6), for by adjusting the magnification M in recording the original speckle photograph, the system sensitivity can be altered to accommodate the amount of motion anticipated in the experiment. This holds regardless of the data reduction method to be used; Young's fringe for point-by-point analysis, or Fourier filtering for full-image reconstruction. Further, the Fourier filtering approach permits a fur-

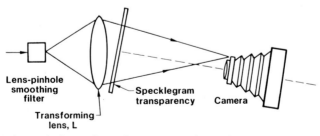

Lens-pinhole
smoothing
filter

Specklegram
transparency   Camera

Transforming
lens, L

FIG. 9.   A practical experimental arrangement for performing a full-image analysis of a specklegram transparency.

ther degree of latitude in sensitivity selection by varying the distance of the aperture from the optical axis for a particular azimuth. There are, of course, practical limitations, especially with regard to recording of the original speckle photograph, established by speckle size, film resolution characteristics and the like, which are considered in Section VI.

4. *Double-Aperture Speckle Photography*

Additional variations of speckle photography have been developed for particular metrological problems. For example, defocused speckle photography, wherein there is not a direct mapping of object points onto corresponding image points as in focused speckle photography, is used extensively for measuring the distribution of tilt over a surface. This is most useful in the analysis of stress and strain which rely on the measurement of local slopes. A variation on the defocused method is tandem speckle photography, developed by Stetson and Harrison (1978), wherein two specklegrams are simultaneously recorded. These specialized defocused techniques are considered in Section IV relative to the applications for which they are intended. However, one further focused method is discussed before proceeding to speckle interferometry.

The technique incorporates two apertures in the optical apparatus when making the recording, as illustrated in Fig. 10. As described by Duffy (1974, 1972), this eliminates the need for an additional filtering

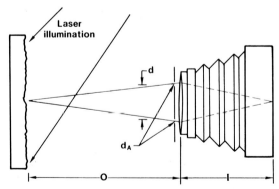

FIG. 10.   Schematic diagram of a double-aperture speckle photographic recording system.

step to observe the fringes, which are a measure of the in-plane displacement between the two exposures of a double-exposure speckle photograph. Further, if desired, using the filtering step, with the Fourier plane apertures situated at points corresponding to those used in the recording step, will provide a bright image with better quality and contrast in the fringes. Alternatively, this two-aperture recording technique also permits the observation of displacement fringes in real time if a single-exposure speckle photograph is recorded of the stationary object, processed, and precisely replaced in the setup prior to the displacement of the object.

Quite clearly, however, the technique requires considerably increased exposure times and/or laser intensity because of the severely limited aperture area relative to recording with a full lens aperture. Furthermore, aperturing such that only areas at the edge of the lens are utilized taxes its image-forming qualities since lenses are generally designed for full aperture use with greater emphasis placed on the center (Stetson, 1975). Finally, both the displacement direction to be studied and the sensitivity with which it can be observed are established prior to recording by the angular orientation and separation of the apertures, respectively. The former limitation can be somewhat alleviated by incorporating four apertures in a cross geometry (Hung *et al.*, 1974; Stetson, 1975). Thus, both x and y components of motion can be evaluated.

Experimentally, the effect of the double-aperture plate can be explained with reference to the sketch and parameters of Fig. 10. By blocking one aperture, or the other, a speckle pattern is formed in the image plane with large speckles (relative to full-aperture speckle photography) by virtue of the inverse relationship between speckle size and aperture size. With both apertures open, interference fringes are formed wherever the two speckle patterns overlap. The spacing of these fringes S_I, expressed in terms of the geometric parameters of the figure, is

$$S_I = \frac{\lambda I}{d} \tag{7}$$

and it can be established for a particular optical imaging apparatus by varying the distance d between the apertures. Thus, small local displacements of the object, occurring between the two exposures, in a direction parallel to a line joining the two apertures will generate moiré fringes, which are a measure of the displacements. The distance between the fringes can be established by taking the magnification M of the system into account, producing an inferred fringe spacing S_0 on the object of

$$S_0 = \frac{\lambda I}{Md} = \frac{\lambda O}{d} \qquad (8)$$

The total displacement can then be determined by counting the fringes from the stationary (0 fringe location) position out to the point of interest. As noted earlier, spatial filtering can be employed to enhance the fringe contrast, which is quite low in the initial photograph because of the random nature of the speckles that cause transparent areas in the processed film. One final observation is apropos. The theoretical number of moiré fringes N_M that can be generated can be approximated by dividing the separation of the apertures d by the aperture diameter d_a (Duffy, 1972)

$$N_M = \frac{d}{d_a} \qquad (9)$$

Simply to point out the enigma of terminology noted in the introduction, this double-aperture speckle photography serves as a proper transition to the topic of speckle interferometry, for many would, and some do, prefer to classify it as such. Their reasoning seems clear considering the interference phenomena involved.

B. SPECKLE INTERFEROMETRY

As one would expect, speckle interferometry involves the combining of two optical fields, generally in what seems a more distinct and obvious physical arrangement than the simple addition of a double aperture to the system as described in the previous section. The subtleties of the distinction are well expressed by Stetson (1975) who considers the process to be speckle photography when there are well-correlated regions in the two speckle pattern images of the optical fields; the fringes resulting simply from translation of the two speckle patterns. When the fringes are derived from fluctuations in the correlation of the two speckle patterns (translation or not), Stetson calls it speckle interferometry. The two optical fields that are combined to perform speckle interferometry may both be speckle fields or, in a manner reminiscent of holography, a speckle field (object beam) and a reference wave; indeed, the sensitivities achieved in this latter case are comparable to those of interferometric holography. Very briefly, the addition of a reference wave restores the capability of sensing a relative phase change when the object moves axially, i.e., parallel to its surface normal, as opposed to speckle photography (Section III,A), which is useful for in-plane translation but very insensitive to normal motion. Consequently, speckle interferometry is especially useful for vibration analysis, as will be clarified subsequently and in the following section on applications.

The variety of speckle interferometer configurations seems almost directly proportional to the number of experimentalists working in the field. For example, as suggested by Hung and Taylor (1974), the addition of parallel glass plates in front of the two lens apertures of the double-aperture speckle photographic system will convert it to a speckle-shearing interferometer by introducing tilt into one of the glass plates. However, the present section shall only attempt to provide the basic forms of speckle interferometers, with the details of subtle variations left to the references cited. Before proceeding, note should be made of the fact that most certainly Leendertz was responsible for the first discussion of this topic at an ICO conference in 1969, with a publication thereafter in 1970 (Leendertz, 1970a, b). Thus, chronologically, the development and implementation of speckle interferometry preceded that of speckle photography, probably accounting for some of the confusion in terminology.

1. Reference Wave Speckle Interferometry

An excellent example of speckle interferometry as achieved with the addition of a reference wave is the design introduced by Stetson (1970). As illustrated in Fig. 11, the system is well suited to the visual study of vibration and movement. In the particular configuration illustrated, there are five optical components, along with an entrance and exit aperture: two achromatic doublet lenses, a wedged beam splitter, a polarizer, and an Amici prism. The two doublet lenses, spaced by the sum of their focal lengths, act as a telescope, and doublets are utilized because of their reasonable correction for spherical aberration; they are positioned so as to form a good image of the entrance aperture (located one focal length in front of the objective lens) in the plane of the observer's eye. The beam splitter serves to introduce the reference beam, and is wedged to eliminate interference of the back surface re-

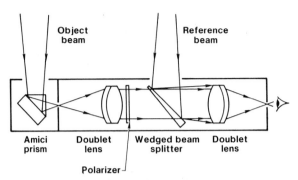

FIG. 11. Schematic diagram of a speckle interferometer for the visual study of vibration, but adaptable to photographic or video equipment.

flected beam, which will be blocked by the exit aperture. The polarizer is located just behind the first doublet, prior to introduction of the reference beam, and where the object field rays are essentially parallel. An Amici prism was chosen to turn the object beam 90° and provide the convenience of having the object and reference beams come from the same general direction. With this element, the inverted and reversed image presented by a telescope is corrected both left to right and top to bottom. Finally, the exit aperture is made adjustable to permit varying the speckle diameter to a convenient size for viewing.

This instrument is ideally suited to the qualitative study of vibrational characteristics. The areas that are stationary, or nodal regions, maintain a high contrast, whereas those areas in motion tend to blur out the speckle pattern reducing the contrast markedly. Thus, as used by Stetson (1978a), in the system illustrated in Fig. 12, it nicely complements holographic interferometry, since speckle interferometry can be employed for the rapid visual assessment of the vibrational resonant modes and time-average holograms can be recorded of those modes requiring a detailed, quantitative analysis.

2. Dual Speckle-Field Interferometry

Whereas the preceding approach can be thought of as a Michelson interferometer with one of the mirrors replaced with a diffuse surface, the techniques to be described herein that incorporate two speckle fields can be thought of similarly with both mirrors replaced, or perhaps as a Twyman–Green interferometer since collimated beams are generally employed. These are the systems introduced by Leendertz in his previously referenced papers (Leendertz, 1970a, b).

The basic geometry of a speckle interferometer for the measurement of in-plane displacement is illustrated in Fig. 13 along with a schematic of one particular experimental apparatus employed by Archbold and Ennos (1974) for realizing the required geometry. As seen in the figure, the two collimated, coherent beams illuminating the object are symmetrically oriented with respect to the YZ plane (both at an angle θ). Thus, any changes in optical path length as a result of translation in the Z (axial displacement, parallel to the surface normal) or Y directions are identical for both beams, and will not give rise to any change in the relative phase of the two independent coherent speckle patterns due to each beam. However, an X-direction displacement u will cause a phase change of $(2\pi/\lambda)\sin\theta u$ for one pattern and $-(2\pi/\lambda)\sin\theta u$ for the other pattern, resulting in a total relative phase change Δ of:

$$\Delta = \frac{4\pi}{\lambda}\sin\theta u \qquad (10)$$

If the surface undergoes a nonuniform displacement, the resultant fringe pattern, obtained in real-time or by double-exposure photogra-

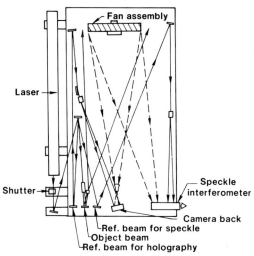

FIG. 12. Schematic diagram of a system for vibration analysis combining real-time operation via the speckle interferometer of Fig. 11 with time-average interferometric holography for permanent records.

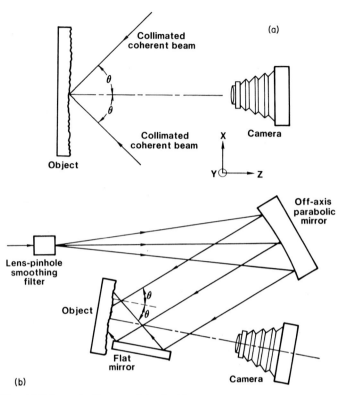

FIG. 13.   (a) Schematic diagram of the dual-beam speckle interferometric method for measuring in-plane displacement, and (b) a practical configuration for its implementation.

phy, is a contouring of displacement in the X direction. The technique is thus sensitive to very small movements, with the incremental displacement between two adjacent fringes equal to $\lambda/(2 \sin \theta)$. Consequently, the sensitivity can be controlled by varying the angle θ, with the maximum measurable displacement controlled by the speckle size. An example of such a technique is presented in Fig. 14, which shows the fringe pattern so obtained, depicting the in-plane displacement along the longitudinal axis of a cantilever beam loaded at its free end.

Truly representative of the classical Michelson and Twyman–Green interferometers is the configuration illustrated in Fig. 15. Here the beam splitter allows both the simultaneous illumination and simultaneous imaging of the diffusely reflecting object and reference surfaces.

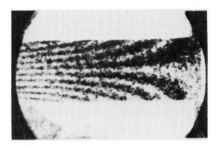

Fɪɢ. 14. Fringe pattern depicting the horizontal in-plane displacement of a cantilever beam loaded at its free end. From Hung (1978).

Such an arrangement measures the out-of-plane displacement, for as the object surface is deformed, only its axial movements contribute to a relative phase change of the two speckle wavefronts. Displacement of the entire surface in an axial direction, changing the relative phase, will reduce the correlation between the speckle patterns from the two surfaces. When the phase change so created is an odd multiple of π, the correlation will be zero; and when it is zero or an even multiple of π they will correlate as before the movement. To detect the position of correlation the real-time method of recording the initial image (before movement of the object surface) and replacing the processed negative in the original position can be used. Proper alignment of the positive ("live" image plane field) and negative fields will essentially reduce the transmission to zero. Subsequent, nonuniform axial deformation

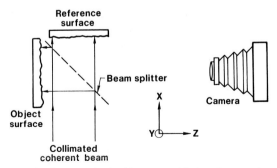

Fɪɢ. 15. Schematic diagram of a dual-beam speckle interferometric arrangement for measuring out-of-plane displacement.

of the object will give rise to fringes representing contours of equal changes in the relative phase, or constant displacement of the object surface, across the image. They are however, somewhat low in contrast, and although other readout methods are available (Ennos, 1975; Tiziani, 1978), they still are limited in practical application.

Still a third configuration, and one especially suitable for out-of-plane displacement, though sensitive to X-direction movement, is that illustrated in Fig. 16. This technique is a variation of the one illustrated in Fig. 13, which consists of placing both collimated beams on the same side of the Z axis at angles θ_1 and θ_2, rather than symmetrically placed on either side of the axis. In this case, a Z-direction displacement w will cause a relative phase shift Δ between the two speckle patterns which can be expressed as

$$\Delta = \frac{2\pi}{\lambda} (\cos \theta_1 - \cos \theta_2) w \tag{11}$$

For the study of general movement where the out-of-plane displacement dominates (e.g., in the case of a flexed plate), the relative phase change between the two speckle patterns is given by

$$\Delta = \frac{2\pi}{\lambda} \{(\cos \theta_1 - \cos \theta_2)w$$
$$+ (\sin \theta_1 - \sin \theta_2)u\} \tag{12}$$

With much larger out-of-plane displacement ($w \gg u$), this expression reduces to Eq. (11) if relatively large illumination angles are used (i.e.,

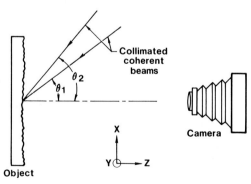

FIG. 16.   Variation of the dual-beam speckle interferometric method of Fig. 13 for the measurement of out-of-plane displacement.

θ_1 and θ_2 close to $\pi/2$). As θ_1 approaches θ_2 in angular extent, the sensitivity of the measurement is proportionately reduced, since a much greater w is required to cause the same change in relative phase. Thus, the system has a capability for measuring relatively large out-of-plane displacements. In the limit ($\theta_1 = \theta_2$), the technique resembles the speckle photography methodology discussed previously. An example of this technique is presented in Fig. 17, which depicts the displacement of a centrally loaded rectangular plate clamped along the edges (Hung, 1978). The incremental displacement between two adjacent fringes is 10 μm.

3. Scattered-Light Speckle Techniques

Before leaving the subject of speckle interferometry, note should be made of the fact that the technique is applicable to transparent media in a manner quite similar to the study of diffusely reflecting objects.

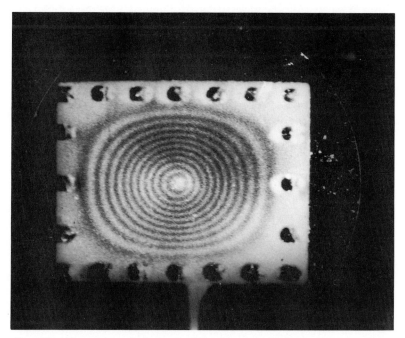

FIG. 17. Fringe pattern depicting the deflection of a centrally loaded rectangular plate as obtained with the system of Fig. 16. (The incremental displacement between two adjacent fringes is 10 μm.) From Hung (1978).

The implementation quite often relies on the recording of light scattered out of the illumination beam, from which the subject heading was derived; indeed, most speckle techniques are based on scattered light but here it is used to distinguish it from diffusely reflected light. Speckle photographic methodology can be similarly extended to the study of transmissive subjects, including gradient refractive index problems such as those encountered in wind tunnel studies for example (Vest, 1979). Examples of scattered-light speckle techniques with transparent subjects are included in Section IV where speckle interferometric measurements of the displacements inside three-dimensional bodies are considered, as well as the utilization of speckle photography for the measurement of fluid flow velocities.

C. SPECKLE-SHEARING INTERFEROMETRY

A final speckle interferometric technique, and one of importance because it measures the derivative of displacement directly, is that which incorporates image shearing. Although the image shearing can be introduced in several ways (Ennos, 1975; Stetson, 1975; Vest, 1979), one straightforward and quite useful approach is that of Hung (1978) and Hung and Liang (1979), which is illustrated in Fig. 18. With this approach the full lens aperture can be utilized, thereby offering im-

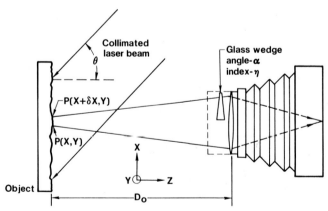

FIG. 18.   Schematic arrangement for speckle-shearing interferometry as achieved with a glass wedge for the direct measurement of displacement derivatives.

proved fringe quality and greatly increasing the light efficiency of the system over the various double-aperture techniques initially reported; as, for example, that of Hung and Taylor (1974). As seen in the figure a thin glass wedge is incorporated over one-half of the camera lens to introduce shear in the image of the object. With the wedge orientation shown, shearing will be in the X direction causing rays from the point $P(x, y)$ to interfere with those from a neighboring point $P(x + \delta x, y)$. With an object distance D_o, and a wedge with index of refraction n and angle α, the magnitude of the shear can be expressed as

$$\delta x = D_o(n - 1)\alpha \tag{13}$$

The presence of shear in the image causes a relative displacement between the two points when the object is deformed, and thus produces a relative optical phase change Δ given by (Hung, 1978)

$$\Delta = \frac{2\pi}{\lambda}\{(1 + \cos \theta)[w(x + \delta x, y) - w(x, y)]$$
$$+ \sin \theta[u(x + \delta x, y) - u(x, y)]\} \tag{14}$$

where u and w are the displacement components in the Y and Z directions, respectively. With small shear, the relative displacements may be approximated by displacement derivatives, reducing Eg. (14) to

$$\Delta = \frac{2\pi}{\lambda}\left\{(1 + \cos \theta)\frac{\partial w}{\partial x}\right.$$
$$\left. + \sin \theta \frac{\partial u}{\partial x}\right\} \delta x \tag{15}$$

Rotation of the camera lens and wedge by 90° (about the Z axis) shifts the displacement sensitivity to the Y axis, and Eq. (15) remains the same with the derivative taken with respect to y.

The previously well-discussed double-exposure recording technique (before and after deformation), when applied to speckle-shearing interferometry produces a speckle fringe pattern depicting the relative optical phase change if the photographic recording is nonlinear. In any event, a high-contrast fringe pattern can be achieved using the previously described Fourier filtering arrangement of Fig. 7 with an opaque stop, rather than a filtering aperture, inserted on the optical axis near the Fourier filtering plane to block the zeroth-order spectrum. With normal illumination (i.e., $\theta = 0°$) $\partial w/\partial x$ only can be measured, as can be seen from Eq. (15). However, isolation of $\partial u/\partial x$ is a more complex process requiring two recordings with different illumination angles and a point-by-point analysis (Hung and Liang, 1979).

Among other most useful implementations of the speckle-shearing technique is that of "shearing by misfocusing," which is discussed in Section IV,B on strain analysis applications of speckle, along with other defocused speckle photographic considerations.

D. WHITE LIGHT SPECKLE TECHNIQUES

Just as in the case of holography, speckle technology has also been expanded to include the use of nonlaser sources. As one example, Boone and DeBacker (1976) have demonstrated both the recording and reconstruction of speckle photographs using white light. Whereas a few materials, such as concrete, have a sufficiently rough surface structure for the recording of white light speckle photographs, in general, special surface preparation is required; retroreflective paint has been used quite successfully. For transmissive speckle studies with transparent models, roughening of the back surface (with the photographic plate placed as close as possible, preferably even in contact) works extremely well. Both white light bulbs and electronic flash lamps have been used as illumination sources.

Once recorded, the white light speckle photographs can be reconstructed with a laser to observe either Young's fringes or the whole-field deformation fringes. In addition, just as Young's fringes can be observed when viewing a "point" light source through a laser speckle photograph, they may similarly be seen in reconstructing a white light speckle photograph with a white light source. However, for making quantitative measurements in such a situation, some form of narrow-band filtering is required to eliminate the "rainbow" effects of diffraction, and thereby sharpen the fringes. To illustrate these effects, Young's fringes from a transmissive white light speckle recording reconstructed with: (1) white light; (2) a He–Ne laser; and (3) filtered white light (6330 Å) are presented in Fig. 19. (Note should be taken of the fact that the "reconstruction speckle," accompanying the use of a laser, is essentially eliminated in the white light results; this is a potential benefit to white light speckle photography.) Similarly, whole-field white light reconstructions from white light speckle photographs are possible with both reflected and transmissive types, although the results associated with transmissive recordings are by far the better, as is also the case with Young's fringe reconstructions.

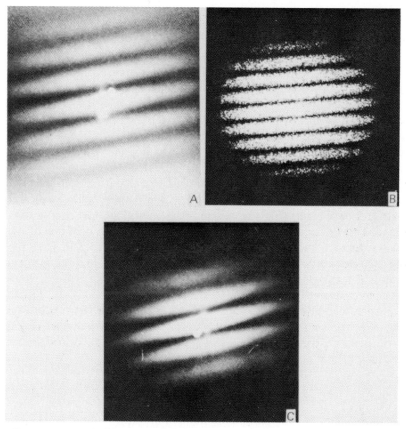

FIG. 19. Young's fringes as obtained from a white light speckle recording reconstructed with (A) white light, (B) a He–Ne laser, and (C) filtered white light (6330 Å). (Courtesy L. C. DeBacker, University of Ghent.)

IV. Applications of Speckle

A. MEASUREMENT OF OBJECT MOTIONS

Speckle technology is extremely well suited to the measurement of object displacement. As already discussed in describing the techniques themselves in Section III, the measurement of in-plane and out-of-plane displacement can be performed with speckle photography and speckle interferometry using the mathematical relationships already presented.

Further, since the methods described were imaging in nature (i.e., the camera was focused on the object), there is a mapping of corresponding points between the object and image. Therefore, the displacements are also measurable even if they vary from point to point across the object as, for example, with in-plane rotation, or with surface strain (the subject of the following section).

Speckle photography is also applicable to the measurement of out-of-plane rotation (i.e., rotations about axes in the plane of the surface), or tilt as it is sometimes called. The theoretical analysis has been detailed by Tiziani (1972b, 1978), and thus the present discussion is limited to a single description and mathematical statement of the result. Considering the schematic illustration of Fig. 20, it can be seen that the basic differences, relative to the speckle photographic method illustrated previously (Fig. 3), are that the film plane has been moved forward to the back focal plane of the lens (i.e., at a distance of one focal length f), and collimated illumination is employed. Thus, each of the speckles are formed by all light scattered in a certain direction, and they will translate as the object is tilted. (The speckle pattern would remain stationary for an in-plane translation.) Utilization of the double-exposure technique (one before and one after tilting the object) and optical processing of the resultant transparency with the system of Fig. 6 will produce fringes with a spacing d_F that can be used to calculate the tilt γ (Tiziani, 1978):

$$\gamma = \frac{f_T}{f} \frac{\lambda}{(1 + \cos\theta)\, d_F} \tag{16}$$

where f and f_T are the focal lengths of the recording and processing

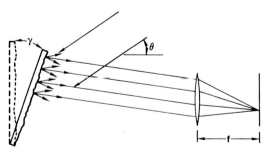

FIG. 20. Schematic diagram of a defocused arrangement for the measurement of out-of-plane rotation or tilt.

lenses respectively, λ is the wavelength, and θ is the angular orientation of the illumination beam used in making the double-exposure recording.

Further in-depth consideration of tilt analysis is available as previously mentioned (Tiziani, 1978). The technique, for example, can be extended to the study of multiple tilts of the object, with an exposure recorded at the beginning and after each tilt. In addition, just as with in-plane displacement, it is speckle size that ultimately sets the lower measurable limit on tilt. While other factors are also involved, it is possible to measure tilt angles down to tens of seconds. Finally, small in-plane movements occurring along with the tilt do not reduce the accuracy of the measurement, but will reduce the contrast as a result of decorrelation of the speckle pattern. However, the converse does not hold. The decorrelation caused by tilt can impose a severe restriction on the measurement of in-plane motion. Although several authors have reported on this subject, as noted in Section II, one approach for expressing the decorrelation problem mathematically has been provided by Tiziani (1978). He states that for good fringe contrast, when measuring a motion that has translated an individual speckle by an amount t, any additional tilt $\Delta \gamma$ should be limited as follows:

$$\Delta\gamma \leq \frac{\lambda}{4(d_{sp} + t)(1 + \cos\theta)} \tag{17}$$

where λ is the laser wavelength, d_{sp} is the speckle diameter, and θ is the angle of the incident illumination in performing the speckle experiment.

Before leaving the topic of object motions, mention should be made of a specialized application of the speckle technique: the measurement of motion paths. In a review article on this subject Wiegelt has considered both lateral motion paths and depth motion, and described various methods of implementation, together with illustrative examples, including real-time techniques (Wiegelt, 1978).

B. STRAIN ANALYSIS

The one-to-one, object-to-image, relationship noted in introducing the previous subject of object motion measurement leads directly to the measurement of in-surface strain. The normal strains ϵ_x and ϵ_y and shear strain γ_{xy} are given by

$$\epsilon_x = \frac{\partial u}{\partial x}$$

$$\epsilon_y = \frac{\partial v}{\partial y}$$

and

$$\gamma_{xy} = \frac{(\partial u/\partial y) + (\partial v/\partial x)}{z}$$

where u, v, and w are displacement components in the x, y, and z directions, respectively. Thus, measurement of the in-surface displacement followed by differentiation provides the strain value. However, of even greater interest is the glass-wedge speckle-shearing technique described previously that was shown to provide a method for the direct measurement of derivatives of displacements, or strain. It should be noted that, in general, the sign of the strain can not be determined after the fact from the double-exposure photographic methods. However, use of the real-time method to visualize the "live" fringes can be used to establish this parameter.

Also of interest are the bending strains in plates, which are proportional to the second derivatives of the out-of-plane displacements ($\partial^2 w/\partial x^2$ or $\partial^2 w/\partial_y^2$). Hung (1978) and Hung and Liang (1979) have demonstrated that by recording a fringe pattern measuring $\partial w/\partial x$, and slightly shifting two such patterns with respect to each other, a moiré pattern is formed depicting $\partial^2 w/\partial x^2$.

Since the speckle-shearing techniques offer a means for avoiding the necessity of differentiation in the calculation of strain, with the attendant potential for errors, it is appropriate to cite a second technique for the study of flexural strains reported by Hung (1978) and Hung *et al.* (1978a), among others. The experimental setup is similar to that depicted in Fig. 18, with the glass wedge removed, and the film plane moved slightly behind (to the right) the image plane of the object. (It should be noted that laser illumination of an object, when observed through an optical system, produces speckles in the three-dimensional space containing the image.) This defocused method has the advantage of permitting selectivity of the derivative direction and sensitivity *after* recording the exposure by using the optical filtering technique of Fig. 7. The results can thus be read out directly as derivatives of displacement with respect to the desired direction, and with greater or lesser sensitivity, just as was done for depicting the horizontal and vertical displacements of Fig. 8. The method is, however, somewhat less tolerant to rigid body rotation, and exhibits poorer fringe quality than the glass wedge technique. In addition, the upper limit of sensitivity to motion is limited by the *f*-number of the imaging system employed. To minimize the effects of this limitation, Hung and Hovanesian (1979) have reported a further extension of the method. By inserting a ground glass in the image plane for the object, with the film plane still slightly to the right (i.e., at its defocused position), the spatial frequency range recorded is greatly increased. (The use of the ground glass can be thought of as increasing the size of the lens aperture— increasing the angle from which light is directed to the film). Hence, the sensitivity range is increased, since it depends upon the size of the diffraction halo, which in turn depends upon the highest frequency recorded. (The Young's fringe data reduction method is employed rather than the full-image optical filtering technique.)

Stetson (1976) has considered the problem of defocused speckle photography and analyzed how the speckles move when the object is deformed, rotated, or displaced. This has opened the way for the application of holographic strain analysis methods to speckle photography (Stetson, 1978a). The key to Stetson's technique of *tandem speckle photography* lies in recording the speckle displacements at two focal planes (neither of which is required to be the image plane), so that the change in speckle motion as a function of focal depth can be determined. This component to the speckle motion results from a slewing of the field scattered from the object toward the observing lens system. It is this field slewing that generates the observed fringes in hologram interferometry and therefore provides the connection between the two techniques. The mathematics of the method are detailed in earlier references (Stetson, 1978a; Stetson and Harrison, 1978).

To describe the implementation of the process, reference is made to Fig. 21, which shows a turbine blade illuminated by laser light. A lens forms an image of the blade surface in the region of two high-resolution photographic plates that are held in tandem by a dual plate holder. The plates are exposed while, for example, the blade is made to vibrate in one of its normal resonance modes. The experiment may be repeated with the illumination striking the object from a different direction. For complete strain determination, three or more independent illumination directions are required. With more than three, the strains are overdetermined and a least-squares-error solution is required.

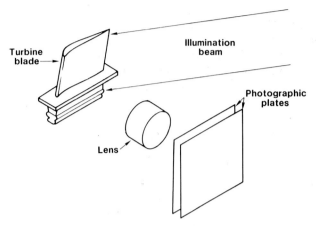

FIG. 21.   Schematic diagram of a defocused tandem speckle photographic arrangement as applied to the measurement of strain on a vibrating turbine blade.

The processed photographic plates (specklegrams) must all be evaluated to determine the speckle motion at the same point on the object. This can be done by replacing them in the holder (one at a time) and performing a Young's fringe type of analysis (Fig. 22). The speckle structure will cause a halo of light to be directed away from the zero order. The doubling of the speckle pattern due to the object vibration will cause fringes to appear in the halo that relate to the magnitude and direction of the speckle motions. Furthermore, light scattered back from the specklegram will pass through the lens and be imaged on the turbine blade, thus identifying the point on the object that corresponds to the point on the specklegram being evaluated.

When all the specklegrams, for a given object point, have been evaluated, the resulting data may be processed to derive the surface strains and rotations of the object. If data, with respect to the local surface normal of the object, is incorporated, the strains may be separated from the rotations. An example of such a strain determination at four points is presented in Fig. 23 for a single-crystal turbine blade excited into its first bending mode. The principal strains are plotted as arrows at several neighboring points on the blade surface, along with the measured strain gauge values for one of the points.

This technique not only provides a complete determination of the strains on the object surface, it also provides complete information as to the rotations of the surface element (Stetson, 1979). Data is obtain-

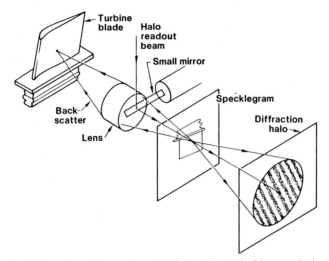

FIG. 22.   Schematic of the arrangement for the Young's fringe analysis of speckle-grams recorded as in Fig. 21 and illustrating how the point being measured is identified on the blade.

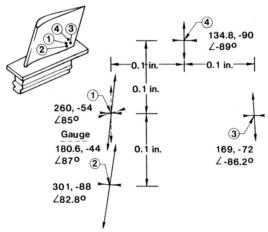

FIG. 23.   Results of a strain analysis for a turbine blade showing the principal strains as arrows for four points within a 0.2 in. square, along with the strain gauge values for point 1.

able in the range from 100 to 2000 microstrain to within an accuracy of ±20 microstrain. For overdetermined solutions, error estimates can be included in the computations.

It should be noted that exactly the same procedure can be followed using three or more hologram recordings of the object. The speckle technique, however, aside from being more tolerant of certain object motions, allows measurement of strain in a range at least an order of magnitude greater than holography. Furthermore, the fact that the measurements are made at very high strain levels allows a smaller region of the object to be sampled in the measurement. The results presented in Fig. 23 are from a region that spans only a few tenths of an inch on the turbine blade, and the area from which each measurement is taken is on the order of 0.050 in. The accuracy of strain measurements made with holographic interferometry and speckle photography, with use of high-resolution optoelectronic evaluation in both cases, has been estimated and compared by Dändliker (1980).

C. VIBRATION ANALYSIS

The double-exposure focused speckle photographic technique of Section III,A, applicable to in-plane translation measurement, can be extended to a time-averaging process for the analysis of in-plane vibration. Just as time-average holography extends double-exposure holography (generally for out-of-plane motion, however) by smearing out the "image," so the speckles form lines with varying exposure between two positions determined by the extremes of the motion, with the zero-velocity endpoints receiving the greatest exposure. The mathematical analysis of Tiziani (1971, 1978) demonstrates that zero-order Bessel function fringes are obtained upon performing the Young's fringe analysis, rather than the cosine fringes of the double-exposure case. In the final analysis, the amplitude T of the vibration can then be evaluated by measuring the separation d_F of the first minima and taking into account any magnification M in recording the speckle photograph (Tiziani, 1978)

$$T = 0.76 \frac{\lambda f_T}{M d_F} \tag{19}$$

where f_T is the focal length of the lens used in forming the Young's fringes.

By employing stroboscopic illumination only at the extreme positions of motion, we return to the Young's cosine fringes of the double-exposure case. The results presented in Fig. 24 illustrate the Young's fringes obtained upon optically processing both stroboscopic and time-averaged speckle photographs of a harmonically oscillating object.

This technique has also been extended to more complex motions than the simple harmonic motion just depicted. Archbold and Ennos (1975) have published results for in-plane vibratory motions that are orthogonal and at rational frequencies where, for example, the processed specklegram yields a lissajous figure. In addition, defocused speckle photography, as described for the measurement of tilt, may also be used for the study of angular vibration. A good illustration of applying speckle photographic vibration analysis to an engineering problem was provided by Tiziani in his investigation of the superposed movements of an oscillating tuning fork from an electronic watch (Tiziani, 1972a, 1978).

For out-of-plane vibration, a modified imaging speckle photographic

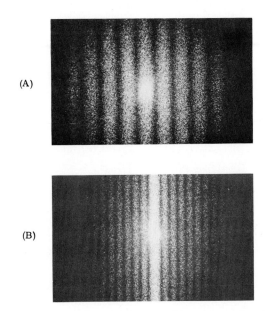

(A)

(B)

FIG. 24. Young's fringes obtained from speckle patterns of an in-plane harmonic oscillation for (A) stroboscopic illumination and (B) a time-average recording. From Tiziani (1978).

technique, attributed to Eliasson and Mottier (1971) (see also Tiziani, 1978) can be employed. The modification involves the use of a diffuser in the illumination beam, with the sensitivity to vibration amplitude controlled by the granularity of the diffuser or, alternatively, its distance from the object. The technique is useful for the detection of nodal lines, for the stationary areas maintain a high contrast that gradually decreases for areas of increasing vibration amplitude. The resultant pattern can be recorded directly by taking advantage of the nonlinearity of photographic emulsions. [This technique has been mentioned previously throughout the article, and briefly stated suggests that speckle intensities above average are clipped due to the saturation of the emulsion, and intensities lower than average are imaged quasilinearly (Tiziani, 1978)]. An example of the technique is presented in Fig. 25, showing a direct recording of the nodal vibration pattern for a piece of aluminum excited at a frequency of 2 kHz. (Spatial filtering can be

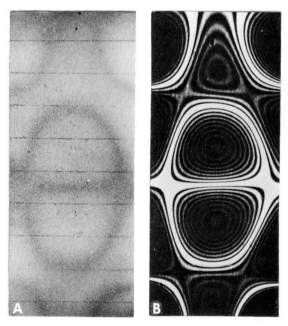

FIG. 25. The vibration pattern for an aluminum plate as obtained (A) with a diffuse illumination speckle technique and (B) holographically. From Eliasson and Mottier (1971).

used to enhance the contrast, and a result obtained with holographic interferometry is included to illustrate the differences.)

The more familiar form of vibration analysis is, of course, that performed by speckle interferometry for the study of vibration mode patterns. The visual speckle interferometer due to Stetson (Section III, B,1) is ideally suited to this problem. In addition, as will be noted in Section V, ESPI has been extensively utilized for such work, and is quite adaptable to vibration phase mapping and amplitude measurement.

D. Speckle Contouring

The well-developed methods of holographic contouring can also be adapted to speckle methodology. Both the multiple refractive index technique (Hung, 1978; Hung *et al.*, 1978b), and two-wavelength method (Ennos, 1975) have been demonstrated, with the latter used quite extensively with ESPI (Butters *et al.*, 1978). The multiple refractive index approach has been used with double-exposure, speckle-shearing by changing the refractive medium surrounding the object of interest between exposures. Subsequent Fourier filtering produces a fringe pattern depicting the derivatives of the object contour with respect to the direction of shear. Further, the two-source method has also been used with speckle-shearing interferometry to measure object contours (Hung, 1978). With the dual wavelength process, speckle interferometry has a distinct advantage over its holographic counterpart. Since an imaging technique is used, the position of the object does not shift when the illumination wavelength is changed; the motion of the reconstructed image in holographic dual-wavelength contouring as a result of the necessary off-axis reference beam has severely limited the practical application of the method. (A system for the dual-wavelength method as implemented with ESPI is illustrated and discussed in Section V,C.

E. Surface Roughness

Considerable attention has been given to the measurement of surface roughness by speckle techniques. As indicated earlier, an extensively referenced, comprehensive treatment of this subject is available elsewhere (Asakura, 1978). Several methods have been successfully employed including ones based on speckle contrast both in the image plane and diffraction field, polychromatic speckle and speckle pattern correlation. In general, the measurable scale of roughness increases with the methods enumerated above: speckle contrast is useful for well-polished surfaces (< 0.25 μm); polychromatic speckle applies to moderate surface roughness ($0.2–5.0$ μm); and speckle pattern correlation covers relatively coarse surfaces ($1–30$ μm).

F. NONDESTRUCTIVE TESTING

In addition to the topics considered individually above, a variety of other applications for speckle metrology have been reported, with a great deal of attention given to nondestructive testing and inspection. A few examples are described in the following paragraphs to provide a flavor for the versatility of the methods.

DeBacker has reported on the detection of cracks in concrete using the speckle capability to measure in-plane displacement (DeBacker, 1975). He records a double-exposure speckle photograph (under two different loads), and observes the Young's fringes formed therefrom by scanning the processed photograph with an unexpanded laser beam. At the crack location the fringes disappear abruptly, and reappear on the other side of the crack with a different inclination. The crack width (or widening if it existed prior to the first exposure) may be calculated by measuring the displacement of two points on either side of the crack.

The detection of loose relay contacts, as described by Waterworth and Reid (1975), exploits the interference pattern changes of reflected speckle from randomly moving surfaces (the loose relay contact). The method relies on auditory, rather than visual senses, by using a photodiode whose active area closely matches the average speckle size. The detector output is amplified and fed to earphones worn by the test operator. Constant frequency excitation of the contact assembly changes the light intensity at the detector in a random (loose contact producing a "crackle" in the earphones) or repetitive (good contact producing a pure tone in the ear phones) manner. The technique has been used successfully to test telephone relays of up to 20 contacts in less than one minute, and should be useful for the remote inspection of tightness of small components in large structures (rivets, nuts, bolts, and the like).

Large structures themselves are amenable to speckle inspection as discussed by Gregory (1978). Using defocused speckle photography he has measured the distortions of a large (1-m²) antenna dish, inspected pressure vessels up to 5 ft in diameter to study bulging around simulated cracks, assessed aircraft wing integrity for surface topological buckling (indicating an underlying crack), and examined buckling loads on the joints of solar array booms. The need for diverging laser illumination, as opposed to collimated beams, with large structures can complicate the problem of separating tilt and transverse motions. Gregory has dealt extensively with these topological problems as they affect the analysis and interpretation of speckle photographic data (Gregory, 1978, 1979). Jacquot and Rastogi (1979) have considered the speckle motions induced by rigid-body movements, both theoretically and experimentally in considerable detail. Relevant to this topic is the adaptability of pulsed laser technology to speckle metrology, for the large size of many objects, almost by definition, requires short duration illumination for most practical environmental conditions. Perhaps as graphic an example of pulsed laser utility as any was the work of Stetson and Elkins (1977) performed at an outdoor jet engine test stand. Utilizing an image derotator system developed for performing interferometric holography and speckle photography on objects rotating at speeds up to 10,000 rpm (Stetson, 1978b), and a 1-J double-pulse ruby laser, they demonstrated the feasibility of measuring the blade tip displacement of a rotating fan stage by the Young's fringe analysis of defocused specklegrams.

An additional example of pressure vessel inspection, but on a different scale than the previously noted work of Gregory, is that of Dahlke *et al.* (1976). They used speckle photography to inspect ~6-cm-diam. vessels fabricated from high-energy-rate forged materials to enhance their mechanical properties. With such an approach it was possible to take advantage of the directional sensitivity to vector displacement after the fact. By using the whole-image reconstruction method for first vertical, and then horizontal, surface motion measurement, flaw detection is simplified regardless of the orientation of the defect.

Further illustration of speckle photographic versatility is the high-temperature strain analysis of steel tensile test specimens by D. J. V. Martin (1978). By employing vernier measuring devices in reducing the Young's fringe data, agreement to within 12.5% or better with strain gauge values was obtained. A result cited for one speckle measurement result of 186 microstrain was just 1.6% lower than the mean value of two gauges located 1 in. to either side of the laser beam interrogation point on the specklegram. This particular test was performed with the specimen at 520°C, and the method should apply at temperatures well above the strain gauge range; the potential for narrow-band optical filtering at the laser wavelength would obviate difficulties associated with radiant luminescence from the hot object overexposing the film. In addition, as in all the strain measurement applications, the necessity for mounting gauges at all the potential points of interest is eliminated.

The practical utilization of speckle-shearing interferometry for non-destructive inspection tasks has been demonstrated by Schaeffel *et al.* (1977) in the detection of flaws in fibered composite cylindrical structures utilized in small solid propellant rocket motors and launch tubes. They have demonstrated the potential for qualitatively screening production line output of such items, with an example shown in Fig. 26. The test object was a hollow cylindrical structure 12 in. long by 3 in. in diameter with a 0.040-in. thick wall containing a thin Teflon strip between two helical wraps. The Teflon prevents bonding of the resin, and thereby permits movement between the two layers upon pressurization of the structure. The result of Fig. 26 was obtained with a pressure differential loading of approximately 20 lb/in.^{2} between photographic exposures, using He–Ne laser illumination and an optical wedge angle of 1.94° to produce the shear.

G. Speckle Study of Transparent Objects

Speckle displacement due to both refractive effects and the presence of scattering particles can be used to study transparent objects and fluids. Illustrative of the latter is the work of Barker and Fourney (1977) directed at the measurement of fluid velocities with speckle patterns. They utilized scattered-light speckle photography to demonstrate a technique for mapping lines of constant velocity in a fluid flow. The method provides an instantaneous velocity map over a complete plane, and thus competes very favorably with laser Doppler velocimetry, which only makes a pointwise measurement. Their work points out the further diversity of pulsed-laser speckle methods, for it incorporated a low energy (<0.1-J) double-pulse laser to study the flow across a single diameter in a circular pipe. A standard 35-mm SLR camera was used to record the light scattered at 90° to the laser beam, and the flow velocity was inversely proportional to the fringe spacing in the subsequent Young's fringe analysis. Similiar fluid flow studies have been

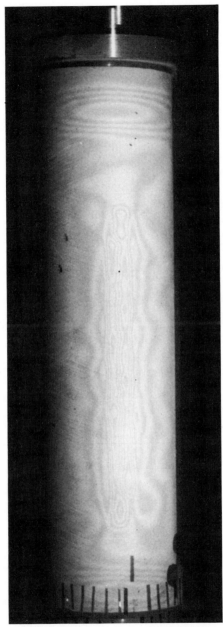

FIG. 26. Example of disbond detection in a composite structure using speckle-shearing interferometry and a 20-psi differential loading. (Courtesy B. R. Mullinix, Redstone Arsenal.)

reported by Dudderar and Simpkins (1980) and by Grousson and Mallick (1977), who used an electrooptic modulator in conjunction with a continuous-wave argon–krypton laser to provide the double-pulse illumination.

A further example of the scattered-light method, but with speckle interferometry, is in its application to the measurement of displacements within Plexiglass materials (Barker and Fourney, 1976a; Fourney, 1978). By limiting the illuminated region of the transparent object to a thin sheet, and arranging the speckle recording system to exclude the direct light, the displacement in that region can be measured when the object is mechanically loaded. Chiang, who has authored numerous papers on speckle, has also investigated and reported on strain analysis methods with scattered-light speckle interferometry (Chiang, 1976). In addition, Barker and Fourney have used this technology to measure the crack-opening displacement relative to the study of the stress intensity factor along the crack front of a three-dimensional crack (Barker and Fourney, 1976b; Fourney, 1978). Luxmoore has also considered the measurement of displacements around crack tips using speckle methods (Evans and Luxmoore, 1974; Luxmoore, 1978), as well as the measurement of crystal-length changes in a nontransparent speckle investigation (Amin and Luxmoore, 1973; Luxmoore and Amin, 1978).

The refractive effect is useful for the study of transparent "phase objects," as with schlieren systems, for wind tunnel flow studies, optical element testing, heat transfer measurement, and plasma diagnostics (Vest, 1979). In this type of study, the double-exposure speckle photographs are recorded, with and without the transparent object present between the camera and a laser-illuminated ground-glass diffuser plate.

Da Costa (1978) has applied speckle technology to the study of transient phase objects, as well as transient reflecting objects in a unique way. The method involved requires the recording of multiple frames of the whole event using motion picture photography. Each successive frame, corresponding to a different instant of time, can then be compared to the preceding frame by an exact superposition to deduce the change in the structure of the object in the corresponding time interval. If, for example, a phase object is studied by mapping the deflection of a fringe system projected through the test field, the pairs of superposed frames will give rise to moiré patterns whose structure is directly related to the refractive index gradient in the test field. The key is to obtain the exact superposition of sequential frames, and this is done by recording a reference speckle field from a stationary diffuser on one-half of each frame. Alignment is then performed by positioning the frames relative to each other until no Young's fringes are obtained on passing a laser beam through every region of the reference speckle patterns. (The use of a spatially random, although time invariant, speckle pattern eliminates any ambiguities in the superposition process that may arise using a reference pattern that has preferential directions or periodicities). The laser beam is then directed through the pair of fringe systems to perform the moiré analysis. Da Costa (1977) has reported an application of the technique to the study of combustion phenomenon. A variant of the method for the transient analysis of reflecting objects, which uses a speckle recording for both the object and reference surfaces (one on each half of the frame), is also discussed by Da Costa (1978).

In summary, the applications of speckle are numerous and of great variety. Only a small sampling has been provided herein to give an idea of its utility. Further, its adaptability to television display (ESPI), to be discussed in the following section, gives it even more potential as an engineering tool.

V. Electronic Speckle Pattern Interferometry

Electronic speckle pattern interferometry, or ESPI, capitalizes on the compatability of speckle interferometry with video-processing technology to offer a user-oriented system suggesting its potential for practical engineering applications in industry. Indeed, entire ESPI systems are commercially available, just as in the case of visual and photographic recording speckle devices, to be discussed in Section VI. An example of commercially available electronic speckle interferometric equipment is the system illustrated in Fig. 27, which is based on research and development performed at Loughborough University of Technology under the direction of John N. Butters (Butters *et al.*, 1978). As shown, this particular device consists of two basic units: the test specimen table (including the laser, optics, and TV camera), and the electronics control package (including the TV monitor).

In its simplest form, ESPI can be thought of as employing closed-circuit television (CCTV) to replace the lenses and films (cameras) utilized in speckle interferometry. With such a configuration, one has a system that is quite akin to time-average holographic interferometry,

FIG. 27.   An ESPI system applicable to a variety of laser speckle measurement and inspection tasks.

and thus directly applicable to vibration analysis. However, with the proper electronics, ESPI can also be used to perform the double-exposure recordings of "conventional" speckle techniques, described earlier, by storing an image of the test object in its initial or reference state for processing with a second recorded later in time. Similarly, with electronic subtraction of the stored video recording from a "live" recording of the test object in subsequent states of deformation, a technique analogous to real-time holographic interferometry is achieved.

A block diagram of an ESPI system with various electronic processing schemes applicable to a wide range of interferometric configurations is presented in Fig. 28. This particular example, from the work of Butters, represents just one of many possible experimental layouts and quite graphically depicts the potential versatility of ESPI. In addition to a direct camera to monitor link, with or without an intervening frequency filtering stage, the video storage and subtraction modes of

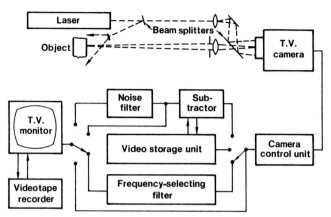

FIG. 28.   Block diagram of a typical ESPI system showing both (top) the experimental optical layout, and (bottom) the electronic control equipment.

operation are provided. Further, videotape recording can be incorporated to provide a permanent record when desired.

Illustrative of the variety of experimental techniques possible is the system of Slettemoen (1980), which uses a speckle reference beam rather than a specular reference beam as in Fig. 28. Speckle reference beams, first introduced in holography (Waters, 1972), eliminate the need for a glass wedge, which is often used on the front glass plate of the TV camera in ESPI work to eliminate the extraneous Fabry–Perot fringe pattern caused by internal reflections in that plate. The method does offer some other advantageous features, but generally the fringe quality is not as good as with a specular reference beam (Slettemoen, 1980).

ESPI has been applied to many problems, similarly explored with both holography and speckle, including such areas as vibration mapping, deformation and displacement measurement, strain visualization, contouring and surface roughness monitoring; the latter two involving dual-wavelength techniques. Similarly, then, it also has application to nondestructive testing, just as holography or speckle do, where unique characteristics in the vibration patterns, or anomalies in the fringe pattern generated by a controlled deformation (whether by thermal, acoustic, pressure, or mechanical means), represent defect areas in an object under inspection. It is only the intent here to provide a few illustrative examples to indicate the type of results attainable, with the detailed discussion left to the referenced material.

A. Displacement Measurement and ESPI

The video display of in-surface displacement for the investigation of strain fields is shown in Fig. 29. The fringe patterns therein were produced by a uniaxial tension on a notched and holed specimen, for both horizontal and vertical displacement measurement geometries (Butters *et al.*, 1978). In this type of study an optical system of the type in Fig. 13a is employed and the initial object state is recorded on a videotape recorder or video storage disc, thus corresponding to the first exposure in a double-exposure photographic process. The video signal of the object under tension, as detected "live," is then electronically subtracted from the stored image, and full wave rectified causing the speckle pattern correlation fringes to be displayed on the monitor. High-pass filtering is used to enhance the displayed image by removing the slowly varying brightness levels.

B. Vibration Analysis and ESPI

The qualitative vibration analysis of resonance mode patterns is quite straightforward, simply requiring the filtering and rectification of the live signal before display. The optical system is generally of the type shown in Fig. 28 (or that of Stetson's visual speckle interferometer in Fig. 11), incorporating an in-line reference beam, since it is the normal component of motion that is usually of interest. Presented in Fig. 30 are some typical results, as photographed from a TV monitor, to illustrate the capabilities of ESPI for vibration visualization (Butters *et al,.* 1978). The figure includes an example of the increased number of fringes that can be observed with stroboscopic techniques. [If the accompanying loss in resolution is tolerable, the poorer light economy of stroboscopic illumination can sometimes be offset with the use of silicon target vidicons (Pedersen *et al.*, 1974; Butters *et al.*, 1978), which have a much better low-light level capability than the standard vidicons.] Generally, as many as five or six fringes can be resolved if care is taken in setting up and performing such experiments. However, with a dual-slit aperture incorporated in the imaging system, it has been reported that sufficient contrast can be achieved to observe 15 fringes

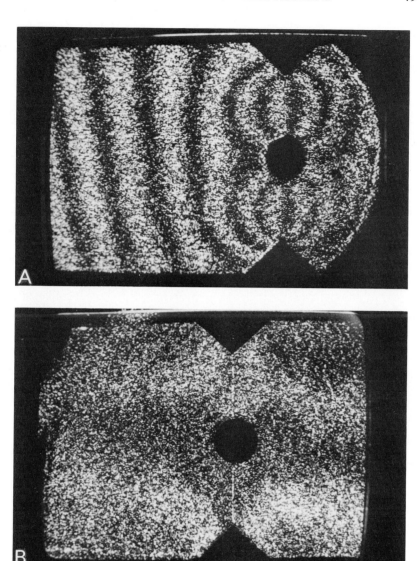

FIG. 29.   The fringe patterns produced by a uniaxial tension on a notched and holed specimen, as observed with (A) a horizontal-axis illumination geometry, and (B) a vertical-axis illumination geometry. From Jones (1976).

FIG. 30. Examples of time-averaged vibration mode viewing with ESPI showing: a square plate, centrally mounted and excited at one edge, (A) with and (B) without pulsed modulation of the laser beam; and a circular plate having a 6-in. diameter, centrally mounted, and vibrating at (C) 10 kHz and (D) 20 kHz. From Butters *et al.*, (1978).

of a sinusoidal vibration on a TV monitor (Biedermann *et al.*, 1976). In addition, the utilization of pulsed lasers in conjunction with ESPI for the study of vibration has also been reported (Hughes, 1976).

Further, scan converter memories (essentially an image tube with associated electronics to permit long-time display of a stored picture) can be used in place of the videotape or disc recorder for storage of the reference state of the object in ESPI work (Løkberg *et al.*, 1976). [The use of electronic storage tube devices was suggested by Macovski *et al.* (1971) for time-lapse interferometry at approximately the same time that Butters and Leendertz (1971a, b, c) reported on electronic signal subtraction for television display of deformation fringe patterns.] The concept of reference wave modulation, used extensively with holography (Aleksoff, 1974), has also been adapted to ESPI for vibration anaylsis studies (Løkberg and Høgmoen, 1976a), providing a vibration phase mapping capability (Løkberg and Høgmoen, 1976b) and extending the lower measurable amplitude range to <1 Å (Høgmoen and Løkberg, 1977).

One such experimental system for these types of investigations, as used in the three preceding references, is schematically illustrated in Fig. 31. A dramatic example of its phase-mapping capability is presented in Fig. 32, which depicts preliminary results of the vibratory response of a human ear drum (tympanic membrane) *in vivo* (Løkberg

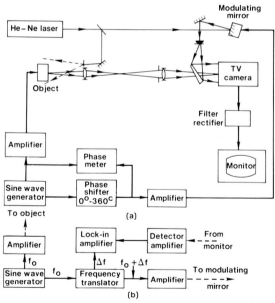

FIG. 31. Schematic of apparatus for (a) vibration phase mapping and (b) amplitude measurement using a phase-modulated reference wave in conjunction with ESPI. (Courtesy K. Høgmoen and O. L. Løkberg, University of Trondheim.)

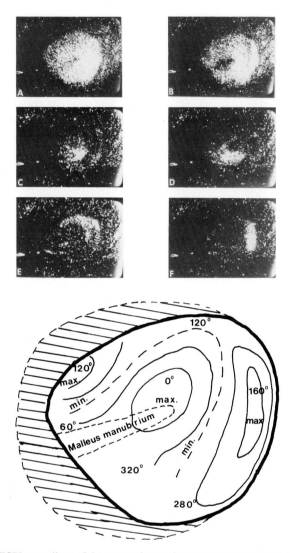

FIG. 32.   ESPI recordings of the tympanic membrane (A) at rest, (B) vibrating at 2400 Hz (standard time-average recordings), and with reference wave modulation for phase settings of (C) 0°, (D) 25°, (E) 120°, and (F) 160°. The sketch shows the isoamplitude lines with maximum and minimum amplitudes shown along with the phase values; the cross-hatching represents an area that was unobservable. [Courtesy O. L. Løkberg, University of Trondheim, and from Løkberg *et al.* (1979).]

et al., 1979). The membrane was excited at 2400 Hz by the free field sound from a loudspeaker, with the sound pressure level (90 dB for the results shown) monitored by a microphone in close proximity to the ear. Using the photographs of Fig. 32 as recorded from the TV monitor and analysis of, and photoelectric measurements from, video recordings [motion of the bright zero-order fringe is more easily observed "live" on the monitor by use of a continuous phase shift (Høgmoen and Løkberg, 1977) than from the photographs], the isoamplitude lines were sketched as shown in the figure. [For the nonmedically oriented reader, vibration amplitude measurements, in the 1–20 Å range, of piezoelectrically excited turbine blades have also been reported by the same authors (Høgmoen and Løkberg, 1977), and are reviewed in Erf, 1978.] Subsequent extension of this work (Løkberg, 1979) has incorporated a synchronous rotating chopper in the output beam of the laser in Fig. 31 to effectively shorten the exposure time of each TV frame making it possible to study both: (1) the sinusoidal vibrations of extremely unstable objects; and (2) the more random motions of, for example, biological objects. An example of the former is presented in Fig. 33, which shows the vibration modal pattern for a *hand-held* circular steel plate 12-cm in diameter; the only stabilizing precaution taken was that the person holding the object also held his breath during the recordings. (Since a continuous-wave laser was used, this is a far cry from the early days of holographic vibration analysis.) The figure illustrates how the effective "stability" is increased as the exposure time is reduced. The exposure time was varied by changing the opening in the chopper wheel and, to partially compensate for the inherent light inefficiencies of such a technique, retroreflective paint was generally used for large objects (remembering that the ear drum is small), and an argon laser was incorporated as the source of illumination. While

FIG. 33. A hand-held circular disk vibrating at 6262 Hz with exposure times of (A) 5 msec, (B) 1 msec, and (C) 0.3 msec. [Courtesty O. L. Løkberg, University of Trondheim, and from Løkberg (1979).]

the "stop-action" capability of such a system does not compete with the submicrosecond pulses of ruby lasers, it does provide the advantage of the high TV framing rate for those problems to which it is applicable.

C. DUAL-WAVELENGTH ESPI

A final example of the versatility of ESPI is in its implementation for dual-wavelength applications: surface contour inspection and surface roughness evaluation (Butters *et al.*, 1978; Jones and Wykes, 1978). A system for such studies can take the form schematically illustrated in Fig. 34 where an argon laser has been incorporated to permit wavelength selection, and thus choice of the contouring interval.

The on-line inspection of surface shape, with feedback control, would serve as an important adjunct to industrial manufacturing processes. The underlying theory of ESPI as applied to such a contouring problem is similar to that of holographic contouring (Varner, 1974). The object under inspection is illuminated with a smooth "master wavefront" at wavelength λ_1, and the speckle pattern interferogram formed thereby is electronically subtracted from a corresponding pattern observed at wavelength λ_2. The speckle pattern correlation fringes

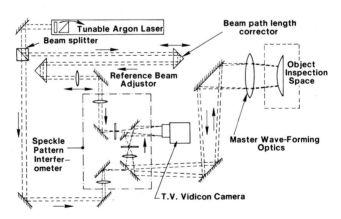

FIG. 34. Schematic diagram of an optical design for applying ESPI to dual-wavelength experiments such as contouring. This arrangement enables the reference and object beams to optically share the same axis. As illustrated, the system is set up for inspecting spherical surfaces, and the equipment includes an argon laser for ease in obtaining the two illumination wavelengths. From Butters *et al.* (1978).

of magnitude $C\lambda_1\lambda_2/(\lambda_2 - \lambda_1)$, where C is a function of the object geometry, thus obtained define the deviations of the inspection object from the "master wavefront." For objects with complex geometries, the "master wavefront" can be provided by first constructing a holographic optical element by using a specular form of the "master" component; the holographic reconstruction is then used to form the "master wavefront." The sensitivity of the comparison may be varied as a function of the wavelength separation and, in the experiments of Jones and Wykes (1978), difference fringes over a contour sensitivity range of 7–25 μm were reported. An early example of the technique is presented

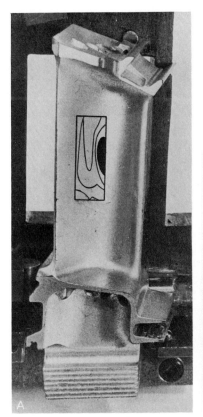
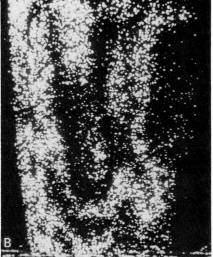

FIG. 35. (A) Turbine blade showing the area and form of the fringe pattern as obtained (B) from the TV monitor with ESPI contouring. From Butters *et al.* (1978).

in Fig. 35 that shows the difference between a master wavefront and a production turbine blade with a contour spacing of 24 μm, corresponding to the wavelength pair 0.496 and 0.501 μm. (The approximate size and form of the fringe pattern is shown diagrammatically represented on the real blade in Fig. 35.)

Successful implementation of this technique assumes that the phase and amplitude of the speckle remain essentially the same for both wavelengths employed. This is approximately true, permitting successful application of the method for specular direction viewing, a small $\Delta\lambda$, and very little fine-scale variation in the surface roughness. Large variations in wavelength and surface roughness lead to a decorrelation of the speckle patterns obtained, and thus negate the method. They do, however, offer a potential method for measuring surface roughness itself. Preliminary experimental measurements of this decorrelation effect have in fact demonstrated that the concept is feasible; and indeed, surfaces of unknown roughness can be measured using ESPI by calibration with surfaces of known roughness (Wykes, 1977; Butters *et al.*, 1978).

VI. General Considerations

Throughout the article several approaches for implementation of the speckle process have been reviewed, and the reader has encountered many examples of speckle technology in its major areas of metrological application: displacement, strain, vibration, and deformation. Note has also been made of its utility to surface roughness investigations and various specialized measurement problems, such as motion trajectories, nondestructive testing, and topology or contouring. It is then the purpose of this concluding section to consider some general topics common to much of the speckle technological field of study. For example, Duffy (1972) compares the sensitivity of the double-aperture technique for the measurement of displacement with the double-beam illumination technique of Leendertz (1970a), and notes the advantages of the former, including the fact that only a single laser beam is required.

It is first appropriate to comment on the fact that the fringe analysis procedures, as described throughout this article, that are required to retrieve highly quantitative data from speckle recordings are somewhat time consuming. This, of course, must be weighed against the impor-

tance of the problem. However, the availability of sophisticated com-
puter-compatible video digitization systems offer considerable promise
for the future automation of the necessary data reduction process to
measure fringe orientation and fringe spacing. (It should also be said
that holographic interferometry shares this same data reduction
enigma.) Indeed, considerable attention is currently being devoted to
this topic. For example, Schaeffel *et al.* (1979b) have described a com-
puter-based system for the analysis of specklegrams and, at the same
conference, Maddux *et al.* (1979) reported on a system to extract both
components of in-plane displacement at a speed of 10 seconds per point
while maintaining a $\pm 2\%$ accuracy in the displacement range of
50–10,000 μin. Of further general interest, on a different subject, was
a report by Schaeffel and his colleagues (1979a) on the use of acoustical
speckle techniques for subsurface work; a development suggesting a
parallel to the manner in which acoustical holography emerged following the establishment of optical holography.

A. FILMS

For the most part, holographic-type emulsions are employed for
speckle recording studies, since both high resolution, to ensure good
imaging of the characteristically small speckles, and a high-modulation
transfer function (MTF) for the range of spatial frequencies in the speckle pattern are required. (The reader should not be misled by the camera schematics provided in most of the figures, since the 35-mm format
is generally quite compatible with most of the techniques, and certainly
more convenient than the characteristic 4×5 glass plates so commonly
associated with holography.) Since good diffraction efficiencies are
necessary, the film should be exposed and processed to achieve high
contrast. Further, bleaching the negative transparencies to a silver
halide, rather than leaving them in a black silver form, generally offers
a better input for the subsequent optical processing step (Stetson, 1975;
Vest, 1979). In this latter step, polaroid films are most satisfactory,
and quite convenient for recording the fringe patterns.

B. SOURCES OF ILLUMINATION

Continuous-wave (CW) He–Ne lasers are quite commonly employed
as speckle illumination sources, but indeed almost any CW laser is

acceptable, as well as some white light methods noted previously. Power as low as 5 mW is sufficient, but of course apertures and exposure times must be adjusted accordingly; thus the trade-offs must be evaluated for a particular problem. Of some significance in this respect is the poorer light economy of speckle photography relative to the holographic process. However, the speckle process is most compatible with pulsed-laser techniques, which became apparent in the discussion of applications. Their utilization for transient events and large objects is, of course, almost mandatory.

C. Measurement Sensitivity Range

Speckle techniques offer a reasonably large and controllable measurement sensitivity range. Cloud has provided a nice discussion on various aspects of this topic (Cloud, 1975). Certainly, of importance at the lower end is the speckle size itself (Section II). In addition, consideration must be given to the object size and magnification, with the latter directly related to the depth of focus. This becomes an important parameter because of the imaging characteristics of the various systems described. For example, the use of small-aperture techniques or demagnification offers a much greater tolerance to axial object motion than the full aperture or large magnification. [Pedretti and Chiang (1978) have reported on the more subtle problem of magnification *changes* in the recorded speckle patterns arising as a result of line of sight displacements due to object deformation between the two exposures.] The available illumination beam intensity also enters this evaluation. Consequently, the practical measurement range will be a function of the particular item under investigation, and the required experimental arrangement. Parks (1979) has devoted an entire paper to the subject of the range of in-plane displacements measurable with speckle metrology, and Chiang and Jaisingh (1979) have considered how the presence of strain affects the maximum measurable displacement. Certainly, motions greater than 1.0 mm are measurable, and the lower limit can extend below 10 μm. (This suggests its complementary, rather than competitive, character with respect to holographic interferometry.)

Quite clearly, the choice of speckle technique will also be dependent upon the subject of interest. The collimated geometries of speckle interferometry will restrict their application to smaller objects, whereas the use of diverging illumination beams, as in speckle photography, are apropos to large subjects.

D. POLARIZATION AND SURFACE EFFECTS

As alluded to when discussing terminology, the phenomenon of speckle itself is one of interference. Thus, as Ennos (1975) has pointed out, a true "fully developed" speckle pattern would require that all light be polarized in the same manner. He also made note of the fact that microscopic changes in the surface structure, as a result of oxidation or wear for example, during the experiment will decorrelate the speckle, negating application of speckle techniques. Ennos further noted that the multiple scattering properties of some surfaces into which light penetrates (e.g., paints, paper, and cardboard) will cause depolarization, altering the brightness distribution from the "fully developed" case, and lowering its tolerance to allowable tilt of the surface.

E. COMPARISON WITH HOLOGRAPHIC INTERFEROMETRY

The brief introductory comment early in the article relative to the appearance of speckle fringes as compared with those of holographic interferometry warrants a few additional remarks. Except for the dual-beam speckle interferometric methods, special vibration isolation is not required as with holography, and the coherence length requirements are generally less severe. (For speckle interferometry, the path-length matching requirements are somewhat less critical than with holographic interferometry). Further advantages of the speckle process include a capability for the independent measurement of in-plane displacement, direct measurement of displacement derivatives, and a wider and controllable sensitivity range, with much of it available after the recording step. They do, however, suffer from a limited tolerance to rotation and total displacement. Care should also be exercised in the selection of optics for speckle studies since certain motions are vulnerable to lens aberrations as reported by Stetson (1977) and others (Archbold *et al.*, 1978).

F. COMMERCIAL EQUIPMENT

Finally, it is of interest to note the degree to which this new technology has already quite firmly established itself. Perhaps as significant a measure as any is the emergence of commercial equipment, designed, developed, and marketed expressly for speckle application, for this opens up the field to the nonoptical engineer who wants to employ the method for a measurement problem. Whereas those investigators intimately involved with research in speckle processes can generally adapt their own existing equipment (cameras, lenses and holders, positioning equipment, and so forth) for experimental speckle work, purchasable systems must be available for the user-oriented applications engineer.

One such item, illustrated in Fig. 36, is a speckle interferometer, patterned after the design by Stetson (1970), which was discussed in Section III, and which is adaptable to visual, photographic, and closed-circuit television display. Another is the laser speckle camera illustrated in Fig. 37, along with its complementary laser specklegram analyzer. The camera, capable of recording two specklegrams simulta-

FIG. 36. A speckle interferometer for visual, photographic, or video applications. (Courtesy Newport Research.)

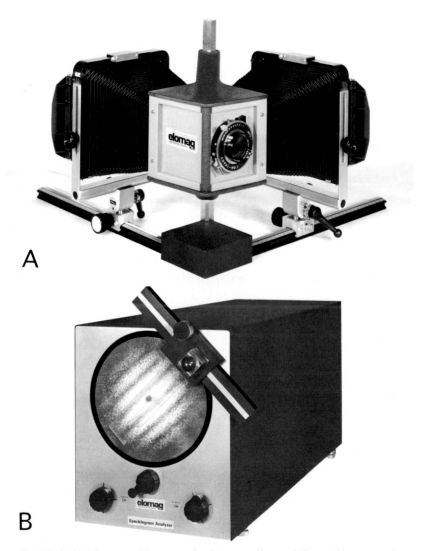

FIG. 37. (A) A laser speckle camera for data recording, and (B) specklegram analyzer for data reduction based on Young's fringes and utilizing $X-Y$ scanning. (Courtesy Elomag.)

neously or consecutively by means of a beam splitter and two independently adjustable film planes, may be utilized for focused, defocused, or incremental speckle photography. The analyzer, with calibrated film translation controls and movable scales, allows one to systematically examine any area of the specklegram. Further, an entire ESPI system is commercially available, as discussed in the foregoing Section V, or alternatively, they (ESPI systems) can be assembled from commercially available components. These units are relatively high in cost, when compared with the visual or photographic recording devices and as such, would generally require a fairly high utilization factor to be economically favorable. In summary, it seems that the potential areas of application, and techniques for implementation of speckle metrology, will continue to expand. Many of these developments, most certainly, will come into routine usage offering rewards in the form of reduced cost or more importantly, as a solution to a heretofore unsolvable problem, and its adaptability to video processing and presentation should have significant impact on its acceptance as an industrial tool.

ACKNOWLEDGMENT

The author would like to express his gratitude to Karl Stetson for his technical contributions to this article, as well as his reading and helpful criticism of the entire manuscript.

References

Aleksoff, C. C. (1974). Temporal modulation techniques, *in* "Holographic Nondestructive Testing" (R.K.Erf, ed.), pp. 247–263. Academic Press, New York.

Amin, F. A. A., and Luxmoore, A. R. (1973). The measurement of crystal length changes by a laser speckle method, *J. Inst. Metals* **101,** 203.

Archbold, E., and Ennos, A. E. (1974). Applications of holography and speckle photography to the measurement of displacement and strain, *J. Strain Anal.* **9,** 10.

Archbold, E., and Ennos, A. E. (1975). Two-dimensional vibrations analyzed by speckle photography, *Opt. Laser Technol.* **7,** 17.

Archbold, E., Burch, J. M., and Ennos, A. E. (1970). Recording of in-plane surface displacement by double-exposure speckle photography, *Opt. Acta* **17**, 883.

Archbold, E., Ennos, A. E., and Virdee, M. S. (1978). Speckle photography for strain measurement—A critical assessment, *Proc. 1st European Cong. Opt. Appl. Metrol., 1977.* SPIE Bellingham, Washington.

Asakura, T. (1978). Surface roughness measurement, *in* "Speckle Metrology" (R. K. Erf, ed.), pp. 11–49. Academic Press, New York.

Barker, D. B., and Fourney, M. E. (1976a). Displacement measurements in the interior of 3-D bodies using scattered-light speckle patterns, *Exp. Mech.* **16**, 209.

Barker, D. B., and Fourney, M. E. (1976b). "Three-Dimensional Speckle Interferometric Investigation of the Stress Intensity Factor Along a Crack Front." UCLA Rep. ENG-7641.

Barker, D. B., and Fourney, M. E. (1977). Measuring fluid velocities with speckle patterns, *Opt. Lett.* **1**, 135.

Biedermann, K., Ekland, L., Ostlund, L. (1976). A TV speckle interferometer, *in* "The Engineering Uses of Coherent Optics" (E. R. Robertson, ed.), p. 219. Cambridge Univ. Press, Cambridge.

Boone, P. M., and DeBacker, L. C. (1976). Speckle methods using photography and reconstruction in incoherent light, *Optik* **44**, 343.

Burch, J. M. (1970). Interferometry with scattered light, *in* "Optical Instruments and Techniques" (J. Home Dickenson, ed.). Oriel Press, Newcastle-upon-Tyne, England.

Butters, J. N., and Leendertz, J. A. (1971a). Holographic and video techniques applied to engineering measurement, *J. Inst. Meas. Control* **4**, 349.

Butters, J. N., and Leendertz, J. A. (1971b). Speckle pattern and holographic techniques in engineering metrology, *Opt. Laser Technol.* **3**, 26.

Butters, J. N., and Leendertz, J. A. (1971c). Speckle pattern interferometry using video techniques, *15th Am. Tech. Symp. Proc., SPIE, Redondo Beach, 1971.* SPIE, Redondo Beach, Calif.

Butters, J. N., Jones, R., and Wykes, C. (1978). Electronic speckle pattern interferometry *in* "Speckle Metrology" (R. K. Erf, ed.), pp. 111–158. Academic Press, New York.

Chiang, F. P. (1976). A new three-dimensional strain analysis technique by scattered-light speckle interferometry, *in* "The Engineering

Uses of Coherent Optics" (E. R. Robertson, ed.), p. 249. Cambridge Univ. Press, London.

Chiang, F. P., and Jaisingh, G. (1979). On the influence of strain in one-beam laser speckle interferometry, *in* "Extended Summaries for the 1979 Spring Meeting (May 20–25, 1979)." Available from Soc. Expt. Stress Anal., Westport, Connecticut.

Cloud, G. (1975). Practical speckle interferometry for measuring in-plane deformation, *Appl. Opt.* **14,** 878.

Da Costa, G. (1977). Study of combustion phenomena by combined deflection mapping and speckle superposition techniques, *Proc. 12th Int. Congr. High Speed Photogr. Toronto, 1976* (Martin C. Richardson, ed.). SPIE Bellingham, Washington.

Da Costa, G. (1978). Transient phenomena analysis, *in* "Speckle Metrology" (R. K. Erf, ed.), pp. 267–280. Academic Press, New York.

Dändliker, R. (1980). Holographic interferometry and speckle photography for strain measurement: A comparison, *OSA Topical Meeting on Hologram Interferometry and Speckle Metrology, June, 1980.*

Dahlke, L. W., Jorgenson, W. E., Saxton, H. J., and Willis, A. P. (1976). "The Performance and Inspection of Flawed Pressure Vessels." Rep. SAND76-8654, June, 1976. Sandia Labs, Livermore, California.

Dainty, J. C. (ed.) (1975). "Laser Speckle and Related Phenomena." Springer-Verlag, Berlin.

DeBacker, L. C. (1975). In-plane displacement measurement by speckle interferometry, *Nondestruct. Test.* **8,** 177.

Dudderar, T. D., and Simpkins, P. G. (1980). Scattered light speckle metrology, *OSA Topical Meeting on Hologram Interferometry and Speckle Metrology, June, 1980.*

Duffy, D. E. (1972). Moiré gauging of in-plane displacement using double aperture imaging, *Appl. Opt.* **11,** 1778.

Duffy, D. E. (1974). Measurement of surface displacement normal to the line of sight, *Exp. Mech.* **14,** 378.

Eliasson, B., and Mottier, F. M. (1971.) Determination of the granular radiance distribution of a diffuser and its use for vibration analysis, *J. Opt. Soc. Amer.* **61,** 559.

Ennos, A. E. (1975). Speckle interferometry, *in* "Laser Speckle and Related Phenomena" (J. C. Dainty, ed.), pp. 203–253. Springer-Verlag, Berlin.

Erf, R. K. (ed.) (1974). "Holographic Nondestructive Testing." Academic Press, New York.

Erf, R. K. (ed.) (1978). "Speckle Metrology." Academic Press, New York.

Evans, W. T., and Luxmoore, A. R. (1974). Measurement of in-plane displacements around crack tips by a laser speckle method, *Eng. Fract. Mech* **6**, 735.

Fourney, M. E. (1978). Scattered light speckle interferometry, *in* "Speckle Metrology" (R. K. Erf, ed.), pp. 281–293. Academic Press, New York.

Goodman, J. W. (1975). Statistical properties of laser speckle patterns, *in* "Laser Speckle and Related Phenomena." (J. C. Dainty, ed.), pp. 9–75. Springer-Verlag, Berlin.

Gregory, D. A. (1978). Topological speckle and structures inspection, *in* "Speckle Metrology" (R. K. Erf, ed.), pp. 183–223. Academic Press, New York.

Gregory, D. A. (1979). Laser speckle photography and the sub-micron measurement of surface deformations on engineering structures, *NDT Int.*, p. 61.

Grousson, R., and Mallick, S. (1977). Study of flow pattern in a fluid by scattered laser light, *Appl. Opt.* **16**, 2334.

Høgmoen, K., and Løkberg, O. J. (1977). Detection and measurement of small vibrations using electronic speckle pattern interferometry, *Appl. Opt.* **16**, 1869.

Hughes, R. G. (1976). The determination of vibration patterns using a pulsed laser with holographic and electronic speckle pattern interferometry techniques, *in* "The Engineering Uses of Coherent Optics" (E. R. Robertson, ed.), p. 199. Cambridge Univ. Press, Cambridge.

Hung, Y. Y. (1978). Displacement and strain measurement, *in* "Speckle Metrology" (R. K. Erf, ed.), pp. 51–71. Academic Press, New York.

Hung, Y. Y., and Hovanesian, J. D. (1979). On a bandwidth extension technique to increase sensitivity of speckle-shearing interferometry, *in* "Extended Summaries for the 1979 Spring Meeting (May 20–25, 1979)." Available from Soc. Expt. Stress Anal., Westport, Connecticut.

Hung, Y. Y., and Liang, C. Y. (1979). An image shearing camera for direct measurement of surface strains, *Appl. Opt.* **18**, 1046.

Hung, Y. Y., and Taylor, C. E. (1974). Measurement of slopes of structural deflections by speckle-shearing interferometry, *Exp. Mech.* **14**, 281.

Hung, Y. Y., Hu, C. P., and Taylor, C. E. (1974). Speckle-moiré interferometry—A tool for complete measurement of in-plane surface displacement, *Proc. 7th Southeastern Conf. on Theor. Appl. Mech.*, p. 497.

Hung, Y. Y., Daniels, I. M., and Rowlands, R. E. (1978a). Full-field optical strain measurement having post-recording sensitivity and direction selectivity, *Exp. Mech.* **18**, 56.

Hung, Y. Y., Turner, J. L., Tafralian, M., Hovanesian, J. D., and Taylor, C. E. (1978b). An optical method for measuring contour slope of objects. *Appl. Opt.* **17**, 128.

Jacquot, P., and Rastogi, P. K. (1979). Speckle motions induced by rigid-body movements in free-space geometry: An explicit investigation and extension to new cases, *Appl. Opt.* **18**, 2022.

Jones, R. (1976). Design and application of a speckle interferometer for measurement of total plane strain fields, *Opt. Laser Technol.* **8**, 215.

Jones, R., and Wykes, C. (1978). The comparison of complex object geometries using a combination of electronic speckle pattern interferometric difference contouring and holographic illumination elements, *Opt. Acta* **25**, 449.

Leendertz, J. A. (1970a). Interferometric displacement measurement on scattering surfaces utilizing speckle effect, *J. Phys. E.* **3**, 214.

Leendertz, J. A. (1970b). *In* "Optical Instruments and Techniques" (J. Home Dickenson, ed.). Oriel Press, Newcastle-upon-Tyne, England.

Løkberg, O. J. (1979). Use of chopped laser light in electronic speckle pattern interferometry, *Appl. Opt.* **18**, 2377.

Løkberg, O. J., and Høgmoen, K. (1976a). Use of modulated reference wave in electronic speckle pattern interferometry, *J. Phys. E.* **9**, 847.

Løkberg, O. J., and Høgmoen, K. (1976b). Vibration phase mapping using electronic speckle pattern interferometry, *Appl. Opt.* **15**, 2701.

Løkberg, O. J., Hølje, O. M., and Pedersen, H. M. (1976). Scan converter memory used in TV-speckle interferometry, *Opt. Laser Technol.* **8**, 17.

Løkberg, O. J., Høgmoen, K. and Hølje, O. M. (1979). Vibration measurement on the human eardrum *in vivo, Appl. Opt.* **18**, 763.

Luxmoore, A. (1978). Measurements of displacements around crack tips, *in* "Speckle Metrology" (R. K. Erf, ed.), pp. 257–266. Academic Press, New York.

Luxmoore, A., and Amin, F. A. A. (1978). Measurement of crystal length changes, *in* "Speckle Metrology" (R. K. Erf, ed.), pp. 247–256. Academic Press, New York.

McKechnie, T. S. (1975). Speckle reduction, *in* "Laser Speckle and Related Phenomena" (J. C. Dainty, ed.), pp. 123–170. Springer-Verlag, Berlin.

Macovski, A., Ramsey, S. D., and Schaefer, L. F. (1971). Time-lapse interferometry and contouring using television systems, *Appl. Opt.* **10,** 2722.

Maddux, G. E., Moorman, S. L., and Corwin, R. R. (1979). A programmable data-retrieval system for in-plane displacements from speckle photographs, *in* "Extended Summaries for the 1979 Spring Meeting (May 20–25, 1979)." Available from Soc. Expt. Stress Anal., Westport, Connecticut.

Martin, D. J. V. (1978). Laser speckle photography measurements of movement and strain in steel structures at temperatures of 20–520°C, *Mater. Eval.* **36,** 53.

Parks, V. J. (1979). The range of speckle metrology, *in* "Extended Summaries for the 1979 Spring Meeting (May 20–25, 1979)." Available from Soc. Expt. Stress Anal., Westport, Connecticut.

Pedersen, H. M., Løkberg, O. J., and Forre, B. M. (1974). Holographic vibration measurement using a TV speckle interferometer with silicon target vidicon, *Opt. Commun.* **12,** 421.

Pedretti, M. G., and Chiang, F. P. (1978). Effect on magnification change in laser speckle photography, *J. Opt. Soc. Amer.* **68,** 1742.

Schaeffel, J. A., Mullinix, B. R., Ranson, W. F., and Swinson, W. F. (1977). "Computer Aided Optical Nondestructive Flaw Detection System for Composite Materials." U.S. Army Missile Research and Development Command, Tech, Ref. T-78-5, September, 1977.

Schaeffel, J. A., Ranson, W. F., and Swinson, W. F. (1979a). Acoustical speckle interferometry, *in* "Extended Summaries for the 1979 Spring Meeting (May 20–25, 1979)." Available from Soc. Expt. Stress Anal., Westport, Connecticut.

Schaeffel, J. A., Mullinix, B. R., Ranson, W. F., and Swinson, W. F. (1979b). Computer aided data analysis system for use in single beam speckle photography, *in* "Extended Summaries for the 1979 Spring Meeting (May 20–25, 1979)." Available from Soc. Expt. Stress Anal., Westport, Connecticut.

Slettemoen, G. Å. (1980). Electronic speckle pattern interferometric system based on a speckle reference beam, *Appl. Opt.* **19**, 616.

Stetson, K. A. (1970). New design for laser image-speckle interferometer, *Opt. Laser Technol.* **2**, 179.

Stetson, K. A. (1975). A review of speckle photography and interferometry, *Opt. Eng.* **14**, 482.

Stetson, K. A. (1976). Problem of defocusing in speckle photography, its connection to hologram interferometry, and its solutions, *J. Opt. Soc. Amer.* **66**, 1267.

Stetson, K. A. (1977). The vulnerability of speckle photography to lens aberrations, *J. Opt. Soc. Amer.* **67**, 1587.

Stetson, K. A. (1978a). Miscellaneous topics in speckle metrology, *in* "Speckle Metrology" (R. K. Erf, ed.), pp. 295–320. Academic Press, New York.

Stetson, K. A. (1978b). The use of an image derotator in hologram interferometry and speckle photography of rotating objects, *Exp. Mech.* **18**, 67.

Stetson, K. A. (1979). Measurement of vibratory strains on a turbine blade by tandem speckle photography, *2nd European Congr. on Optics Applied to Metrology, Nov., 1979.*

Stetson, K. A., and Elkins, J. N. (1977). "Optical System for Dynamic Analysis of Rotating Structures." UTRC Tech. Rep. R77-992054 under Air Force Contract F33615-75-C-2013, March, 1977 (also issued as Air Force Rep. AFAPL-TR-51, October, 1977).

Stetson, K. A., and Harrison, I. R. (1978). Determination of the principal surface strains on arbitrarily deformed objects via tandem speckle photography, *Proc. 6th Int. Conf. Exp. Stress Anal.,* p. 149. Munich.

Tiziani, H. J. (1971). Application of speckling for in-plane vibration analysis, *Opt. Acta* **18**, 891.

Tiziani, H. J. (1972a). Analysis of mechanical oscillations by speckling, *Appl. Opt.* **11**, 2911.

Tiziani, H. J. (1972b). A study of the use of laser speckle to measure small tilts of optically rough surfaces accurately, *Opt. Commun.* **5**, 271.

Tiziani, H. J. (1978). Vibration analysis and deformation measurement, *in* "Speckle Metrology" (R. K. Erf, ed.), pp. 73–110. Academic Press, New York.

Varner, J. (1974). Holographic and moiré surface contouring, *in* "Holographic Nondestructive Testing'' (R. K. Erf, ed.), pp. 105–147. Academic Press, New York.

Vest, C. M. (1979). "Holographic Interferometry," Wiley, New York.

Waters, J. P. (1972). Object motion compensation by speckle reference beam holography, *Appl. Opt.* **11,** 630; see also p. 235 of Erf (1974).

Waterworth, P., and Reid, D. C. J. (1975). Loose contact detection using laser speckle, *Opt. Laser Technol.* **7,** 135.

Weigelt, G. P. (1978). Measurement of motion paths, *in* "Speckle Metrology" (R. K. Erf, ed.), pp. 159–181. Academic Press, New York.

Wykes, C. (1977). De-correlation effects in speckle pattern interferometry I, *Opt. Acta* **24,** 517.

LASER APPLICATIONS: VIDEO DISC

A. Korpel*

Zenith Radio Corporation
Chicago, Illinois

I. Introduction

In 1977 video recording was exactly 50 years old. Abramson, in an excellent review article on the history of television recording (Abramson, 1955, 1973) refers to experiments done as early as 1927, by Baird, the English counterpart of Edison. The reader who checks this reference and manages to get hold of a June 1927 copy of *Radio News*—

* Present address: Division of Information Engineering, The University of Iowa, Iowa City, Iowa 52242.

LASER APPLICATIONS, VOLUME 4

Hugo Gernsback, editor, and filled with nostalgic ads for shiny radio valves and pointed loudspeakers—will find an article entitled "Television Sees in Darkness and Records Its Impressions" (Dinsdale, 1927). Figure 1 is a photograph from that article; it shows Baird demonstrating what he called his Phonoscope, "a machine for preserving radio pictures by means of phonographic records."

In retrospect, Baird had an easy task in implementing his idea; the technology was available. His (own) television system had a resolution of 30 lines at a frame rate of 12.5 pictures per second. It would probably have required a bandwidth of 7.5 kHz for optimum performance, about the same as needed for voice communication. Hence, Edison's wax cylinder lent itself reasonably well to this first experiment in video recording.

Baird was, of course, aware that his TV signals were in the audio range and, characteristically, he decided to listen to the sounds they produced before turning them back into images:

Radio News for June, 1927

Mr. Baird demonstrating his Phonoscope, a machine for preserving radio pictures by means of phonograph records.

FIG. 1. Baird demonstrating the Phonoscope. [From *Radio News*, June, 1927; see Dinsdale (1927).]

For experimental purposes Mr. Baird has some phonograph records made of the sounds made by different persons' faces, and, by listening carefully to the reproduction of these records it is possible to distinguish between one face and another, by the sounds they make.

This must surely have been the first example of pattern recognition by ear!

After describing the final step of recreating the original images by means of a "televisor," the *Radio News* article concludes: "There is room here for the imaginative to indulge in speculation on the scope for future development along these lines." And speculation it remained, for the next 30 years.

Baird's system called for a 7.5-kHz bandwidth; modern television practice, because of much increased resolution plus the addition of color and sound, requires about 4 MHz. If the recording process requires special encoding such as FM, in order to overcome noise and nonlinearities, this must be about tripled. [The recently concluded Philips–MCA–Zenith technical recommendations (Boegels, 1976) call for a 13-MHz capability of the recording medium.] The total bandwidth available on a modern stereophonic record is of the order of 40 kHz. The ratio between what is required and what is readily available is startling: between 100 and 300. This ratio is well illustrated by Fig. 2, which shows, side by side, the grooves on a conventional LP record and the pitted tracks on a modern video disc.

There are two ways to overcome the discrepancy in bandwidth: adapt the source to the recording technique or vice versa. In this article I shall concentrate on the second approach. Nevertheless, the other way of solving the problem is quite interesting and I will discuss it here briefly.

If the rate of scanning out the TV picture is reduced by a factor of about 300, its frequency range decreases sufficiently to record it on a standard LP audio record. This was in fact done by the Westinghouse Electric Co. (*New Products*, 1974) for the purpose of recording still pictures. Two hundred such pictures could be stored on one side of a standard 12 in. $33\frac{1}{3}$ rpm record, which the company named Videodisc. The system itself was called Phonovid and used a storage-type scan converter in the player to convert back to the fast scan, necessary for playback through the home television receiver. Scan converters using image tubes—as this one did—are quite complex and costly; they are not well suited for the mass market. It is conceivable however that the

FIG. 2.   Comparison of audio record (left) and video disc (right). (Courtesy Zenith Radio Corp.)

semiconductor memory-type scan converters of the future may yet make such a system economical, especially for educational purposes.

A second way to adapt the source to the recording material is to reduce its redundancy. By redundancy is meant simply that of the sequence of normal TV pictures, which occur at a rate of 30/sec, one picture is very much like the next one. There should be a clever way of making use of this, to reduce the flow of redundant information and hence decrease the bandwidth. One sophisticated technique of encoding, Sampledot (Stone, 1976), is rather promising in that respect; it is said to reduce the necessary bandwidth by a factor of 10, without introducing too many objectionable image artifacts. It seems likely however, that techniques such as Sampledot will not be sufficiently well developed in time to affect the emerging video-disc formats, none of which uses redundancy suppression.

Let us now return to the question of finding a suitable medium and technique for recording conventional—or at least conventionally en-coded—video. For the sake of argument assume that 30 min of high-quality video is desired and that, for good signal-to-noise, the baseband video is encoded in some, as yet unspecified, way that requires a 10-MHz bandwidth. It is easy to calculate that the total number of cycles to be recorded is approximately $30 \times 60 \times 10^7 = 1.8 \times 10^{10}$. If we use a 12-in. disc as the record format and leave out a central area as is done on phonograph records, there remains an available area of about $5 \times 10^{10} \ \mu m^2$. Hence, one cycle (two samples) occupies about 2.8 μm^2, microscopic dimensions indeed! Most optical engineers are aware of the fact that no mechanical stylus could possibly read such informa-tion—a prejudice which most of us share and which is wrong, as I shall show later—but that a laser beam will do very nicely. A reasonably inexpensive lens (say NA = 0.4) focusing a beam from a He–Ne laser (λ = 6328 Å) produces a spot of 0.75-μm diam. (first dark ring), small enough to read out our record. Choosing a spiral-track recording for-mat, as in audio, it seems reasonable to split up the 2.8 μm^2/cycle evenly between track spacing and track detail, resulting in about 600 tracks/mm and a spatial frequency of 600 cycles/mm along the tracks.

These numbers give a rough idea of what the disc is going to be like, but a few modifications are necessary in the interest of practicality. So far we have tacitly assumed that all tracks have the same maximum spatial frequency, but this implies—for a constant temporal frequency of the carrier—that the linear velocity at each track (i.e., at each radius) be constant. Such an arrangement would require that the rotational disc velocity (i.e., the motor speed) would have to be inversely pro-portional to the radius of the track being read out at a given moment, clearly a somewhat impractical scheme. It is much simpler to keep the motor speed constant and let the spatial frequency of recording increase toward the inside of the disc. This is, in fact, what is done in practice. The rotational speed is usually chosen to be 1800 rpm (30 rps) so that one complete television picture is recorded once around. This makes it possible to let the laser beam jump back from the end to the beginning of each separate picture (i.e., track) so as to freeze motion. We will return to this later. In the recommended standards (Boegels, 1976) a 12-in. disc rotates at 1800 rpm and contains $\frac{1}{2}$hr of programming, re-corded from an inner radius of 5.5 cm to an outer radius of 14 cm. The track density is 600/mm and the highest spatial frequency along the inner track is 1250 cycles/mm. A 0.4-NA lens in conjunction with a He–Ne laser is sufficient for readout.

Naturally, a few mechanical criteria have to be satisfied for satisfactory operation. For one thing, the depth of focus using a 0.4-NA lens is only about 4 μm; the distance between lens and record has to be maintained within this tolerance while the disc is spinning at 1800 rpm! Also, the beam has to follow the track to within a few tenths of a micron. It is, of course, not possible to locate the hole in the center of the disc so precisely; typical eccentricities are of the order of 100 μm and without a beam-steering servo the readout spot would cross about 60 tracks in one revolution. (Whatever may be said of mechanical systems, vertical and radial tracking are simple!) Finally, in order to maintain synchronization and correct color, the timing of signals, read off the disc, has to be correct. For good synchronization the timing error should not exceed more than about one picture element or 125 nsec; good color requires more stringent timing control, to within 8 nsec (Fink, 1975). How optics helps in doing all this will be shown later in this article. First, however, it is necessary to become somewhat more familiar with the present TV format. This is discussed in the next section.

II. TV Format

Figure 3 shows the present TV format as it applies to the United States (Fink, *et al.*, 1975). Each complete picture or frame is scanned out twice every $\frac{1}{30}$ sec. The lines of the two successive scans are in-

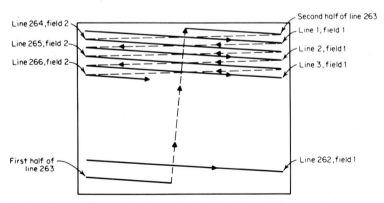

FIG. 3.   Present TV scanning format in the U.S. (From Fink, 1975. Copyright © 1975 by McGraw–Hill Book Company. Reprinted with permission.)

terlaced; each system of lines defines what is called a field. This particular format in which each frame is scanned out twice was chosen because, by increasing the presentation rate from 30 to 60 Hz, flicker is reduced.

Of the 525 lines that form a complete frame, 42 are used for nonvisual purposes such as retrace, synchronization, etc. Thus only 483 lines are visible on the screen. From the point of view of optics, each two lines constitute one cycle of spatial frequency, as two independent samples are required per cycle. Thus it would appear that, in the vertical direction, the TV standards specify a resolution of about 242 cycles. It turns out, however, that the subjective resolution is less than this number because of the fact that the line pattern is fixed on the screen, i.e., its phase cannot be changed. This reduction in resolution is expressed by the so-called Kell factor which equals about 0.7 for TV (Fink, 1952). Taking this into account, we find that the subjective vertical TV resolution equals about 170 cycles.

The aspect ratio of the TV screen is fixed at 4 : 3; hence, for equal vertical and horizontal results the standards should allow $\frac{4}{3} \times$ 170 = 227 cycles across the screen. The time required to sweep out one line across the screen is $(\frac{1}{30} : 525$ sec $\simeq 63.5$ μsec. However, about 11.5 μsec are used for synchronization and color reference signals, leaving 52 μsec to display 227 cycles. Hence, the cycle period is 52 μsec/227 $\simeq 0.23$ μsec; the highest temporal frequency required is the inverse of that number or $\simeq 4.4$ MHz. The official standards actually specify a temporal cutoff frequency of 4.5 MHz as shown in Fig. 4 (Fink et $al.$, 1975).

When color was added to television, room had to be found in the

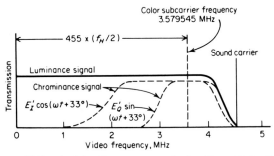

FIG. 4. Present U.S. television frequency standards. (From Fink, 1975. Copyright © 1975 by McGraw–Hill Book Company. Reprinted with permission.)

frequency spectrum to accommodate this new development. At first glance it might seem that, because of the requirement for three primary colors, three times as much bandwidth would have been required. However, by making ingenious use of some physiological effects and exploiting the unique character of the television spectrum, engineers actually succeeded in accommodating the color information within the existing frequency standards. In addition, they managed to do this in such a way as to make the new standards compatible with black-and-white receivers, i.e., the composite color-carrying signal still gives a conventional black-and-white picture on such receivers. It is interesting to see how this was done.

Instead of describing a color by specifying the amounts of its three primary components, it is often more convenient to use three other attributes such as hue, saturation, and brightness (called hue, chroma, and value by artists) (Fink, 1957). "Hue" describes the shade of the color such as "red," "blue," "purple," etc. "Saturation" is the word used for the intensity or strength of the color. Thus, pale green is less saturated than deep green. Finally, "brightness" or "luminance" is related to the total luminous flux received by the eye when looking at an object no matter what its color. In this system of coordinates white has zero saturation and indefinite hue; spectral colors have maximum saturation, their hue being dependent on their wavelength. There is also a range of hues made from a mixture of two pure spectral colors, such as purple, that are perceived as fully saturated.

It is obvious that a description in these terms is of great value to the artist—Seurat, the pointillist painter may have been an exception—and, in fact, a color atlas based on hue, saturation, and brightness was devised by an artist, A. H. Munsell. In the atlas, each color corresponds to a point in a cylindrical coordinate system of finite radius and height. The height denotes the brightness on a scale of 1–10, the radius similarly gives the saturation value, whereas the angle corresponds to hue. In the Munsell atlas, the angle is not explicitly given; rather the circle of maximum saturation and constant brightness is marked off in hue intervals and subintervals denoted by a number-plus-letter combination. Thus 5 YR stands for a specific hue in the yellow–red range.

Now it is interesting that a description of colors, based on artistic needs, should lend itself so well to color television transmission. The main reason is a physiological finding: the description of a colored scene in terms of hue, saturation, and brightness requires full resolution for brightness but only about one-eighth that resolution for hue and saturation. In terms of television, if we transmit these three attributes instead of the three primary colors we need a much smaller bandwidth. Moreover, in black-and-white television, brightness—or luminance— is transmitted already (with a bandwidth of 4.4 MHz as we have seen); hence, we only have to add hue and saturation (with a bandwidth of approximately 0.5 MHz) in order to obtain a complete color picture.

Preferably, adding hue and saturation should be done in such a way that black-and-white TV receivers can easily disregard the extra information which they do not need. A simple way of doing this is to modulate the hue and saturation signals on an extra subcarrier, which can be separately processed in the receiver. Because a carrier at frequency ω is described by two independent parameters—such as phase and amplitude, or the relative strength of the cos ωt and sin ωt components (quadrature modulation)—it is entirely feasible to encode it with two independent signals. Now, in the Munsell color atlas, hue is described by an angle and the degree of saturation by the length of a radius; what would be more logical than to transmit hue as the phase of a subcarrier and the degree of saturation as its amplitude? This is essentially what is done in the American system of color television, where a frequency of 3.58 MHz is chosen for the subcarrier (Fig. 4).

The relationship between phase and hue is shown in Fig. 5 (Barstow, 1955), where we see that the zero reference angle corresponds to pur-

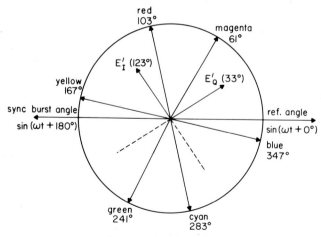

FIG. 5. Color diagram illustrating color encoding by phase and amplitude. (After Barstow, 1955.)

ple, magenta is at 61°, yellow at 167°, etc. The arrow marked "sync burst angle" refers to the phase of a short burst of carrier signal that is inserted prior to the beginning of each TV line to provide a phase reference.

The description of a radius vector in terms of magnitude r and azimuth ϕ is, of course, equivalent to a description in terms of orthogonal coordinates, $x = r \cos \phi$ and $y = r \sin \phi$. Figure 5 shows two coordinate axes E_I' and E_Q'. The magnitude and phase of the subcarrier for any combination of saturation and hue may be described by the corresponding chromaticity components along the E_I' (orange to cyan) and the E_Q' (yellow/green to purple) axes. These particular axes were chosen because one of them (E_Q') represents those chromaticity changes to which the eye—at least with respect to small areas—is least sensitive; this component may therefore be transmitted within a narrower bandwidth (see Fig. 4) than the orange–cyan E_I' component (McIlwain and Dean, 1956). The two subcarrier components E_I' and E_Q' are transmitted by the television station with a 90° phase shift between them. The alternative decription of the subcarrier in terms of the amplitude and phase of the resultant of these two components is more relevant to the video disc, because momentary speed variations in the player interfere with the correct phase of the subcarrier and hence directly affect the perceived hue. We will return to this later.

The reader will have noticed from Fig. 4 that the frequencies related to color are placed inside the luminance spectrum; surely this must lead to confusion in the receiver! As it happens, however, the television signal, because of the scanning, is pretty much periodic with a periodicity equal to the line time of 63.5 μsec. As a result the frequency spectrum is also periodic, it exhibits "holes" spaced 1/63.5 μsec = 15.734 kHz apart. The color subcarrier is located exactly in the center of one of these holes at 3.58 MHz and as a result the color spectrum, also being periodic, interleaves the luminance spectrum. In the receiver the two spectra are unscrambled and processed separately.

It is by making use of this periodicity and exploiting the fact that color (i.e., hue and saturation) only requires about one-eighth the linear resolution of luminance, that television engineers managed to squeeze the color information inside the existing frequency standards.

Apart from luminance and color, sound has to be transmitted as well. The standards specify a special, frequency-modulated, carrier for this at 4.5 MHz.

In video recording it is not mandatory to adhere to the standards as far as the signal on the disc is concerned. All that matters is that the signal reaching the TV set be in standard form and this can be accomplished by electronic reencoding after readout (vanden Bussche *et al.*, 1973). This freedom of choice makes it possible to adapt the encoding to the noise—and bandwidth characteristics of the recording material, as well as to the mechanical limitations of the player. To give an example, in certain systems phase encoding of the color is not used because it requires great speed stability in the player. In another system, the color subcarrier is moved to a lower frequency for the same reason. In this article I shall not discuss such matters as they are mainly of interest to electronic engineers only. Where frequency allocations have to be mentioned, because of their bearing on MTF, depth of focus, etc., I shall limit myself to the Philips–MCA–Zenith recommended standards (Boegels, 1976) with which I am most familiar.

III. Historical Background

Following Baird's 1927 experiments the next quarter of a century saw no more attempts at electronic video recording. Instead, various film recording techniques were developed (Abramson, 1955); photographic film was, at that time, the only medium with high enough resolution. Strangely enough, during those years no consideration appears to have been given to recording TV *signals* on photographic discs rather than TV *pictures* on film. In 1951 the first magnetic recorder for black-and-white TV was developed by Bing Crosby Enterprises, followed in 1953 by the RCA color videotape recorder. It was not until 1961 that the first video-disc recorder was developed for the 3M Company at Stanford Research Institute (SRI) (Rice *et al.*, 1970).

A. SRI–3M

In the SRI–3M player recording was done on an 8 × 10-in. glass plate coated with a high-resolution emulsion. Spiral tracks were laid down with a 1-μm spot produced by a 100-W high-pressure arc lamp, which was also used for playback. A Kerr cell, driven with the video signal, modulated the light. The track spacing was chosen to be 5 μm and the plate was rotated at 1800 rpm. Figure 6 shows a photograph

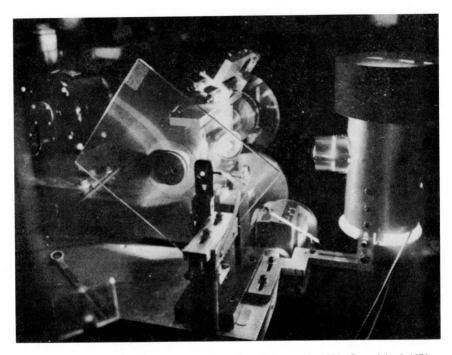

FIG. 6. Early SRI–3M player-recorder. (From Rice *et al.*, 1970. Copyright © 1970 by the Society of Motion Picture and Television Engineers, Inc., Scarsdale, New York. Reprinted with permission.)

of the system. It did not have a tracking servo and consequently, upon playback, the (black-and-white) TV signal was averaged[1] over several tracks; there still remained some unavoidable eccentricity when replacing the glass recording plate after development. The investigators recognized that this was not serious because of the redundant nature of the TV signal; they pointed out that such redundancy does not exist in sound however, and that averaging audio tracks would be intolerable. Consequently, they did not record sound although they devised some ingenious techniques of audio encoding suitable for a track averaging system. The problem of focus stability was solved by mounting

[1] It should be noted that track averaging is usually only possible when, as in the SRI experiments, the TV signal is not encoded on a carrier. The reason is that carriers cannot be averaged unless special care is taken that they are in the same phase on neighboring tracks.

the recording lens on a lightly spring-loaded air bearing (Fig. 7). Focus could be adjusted precisely by varying the air pressure.

This early video-disc work set the basic format of spiral recording at 1800 rpm, still found in modern machines. The SRI method of photographic baseband recording is, however, seldom used nowadays because of noise problems and difficulty of replication. As will be seen later, the modern practice is to use some form of FM encoding on phase relief material. Such a relief recording can be easily and quickly replicated by conventional pressing or molding techniques, well known in the audio record industry. In playback, a focus servo has replaced the air bearing used by the SRI group and tracking servos have made it unnecessary to rely on track averaging. It must be said though that all this has come about at the expense of the simplicity that is so appealing in the SRI machine.

B. TELEFUNKEN–DECCA (TELDEC)

Surprisingly enough the next video-disc player, developed by Telefunken–Decca around 1970, was based on purely electromechanical concepts (Dickopp and Redlich, 1973). Before seeing how this one works, it is interesting to repeat the arguments against a mechanical player, arguments much heard among electrical and optical engineers (my laboratory was no exception) prior to the actual invention of such a machine. The reasoning is as follows: Video recording involves very high frequencies, say up to 3 MHz for a reasonable, if not perfect, picture. Assume that we make a hill-and-dale record such as used in stereophonic audio. The roughness of the disc material is about 100

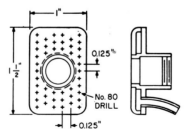

FIG. 7. Air bearing for microscope objective in SRI–3M player (from Rice *et al.*, 1970. Copyright © 1970 by the Society of Motion Picture and Television Engineers, Inc., Scarsdale, New York. Reprinted with permission.)

Å so that, for a reasonable signal-to-noise ratio (say $100\times$), the hills should have a height of 100×100 Å $= 1$ μm. Now, if a mechanical stylus is to read out such a recording, it will have to move up and down a total of 1 μm at a maximum rate of, say, 3 MHz. The accelerations involved are of the order of 2×10^8 m/sec^2 or 2×10^7 g. Let us make the stylus very light, of the order of 1 mg. Then the forces needed to move the stylus are of the order of 200 N or about 20-kg force. The stylus has to be very thin to read out the fine details; let us make the area of its tip 10 μm^2. The pressure on the stylus is then 2×10^{13} N/m^2 or roughly 10^6 tons/in.^{2}! It is obvious that this will not work, so we may as well forget about it.

The Telefunken engineers turned the argument around and, realizing that the stylus would be, to all intents and purposes, immovable, decided instead to absorb the motion in the disc. Their basic invention is illustrated in Fig. 8. The key element is the diamond skid-type stylus that is attached to a piezoceramic transducer. The disc is made of flexible PVC and has a thickness of 100 μm. In operation the disc spins freely, at 1800 rpm, above a fixed platform that stabilizes the motion

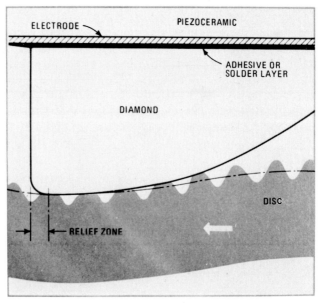

FIG. 8. Teldec pressure pickup. (From Dickopp and Redlich, 1973. Reprinted from *Electronics*. Copyright © 1973 by McGraw–Hill Book Company.)

through aerodynamic forces. As shown in the figure, the peaks of the recording are gradually compressed when the disc passes under the stylus. When such a compressed peak reaches the sharp edge of the skid, it suddenly loses contact causing a sudden reduction of pressure against the stylus. This is picked up by the piezoelectric transducer which then produces an electrical impulse. This type of pickup device is called a "pressure stylus" and, as seen, is distinctly different in operation from the more conventional "motion stylus." It basically counts the peaks of the recording, and hence is very well suited for FM, the encoding technique used by Telefunken in this player.

Figure 9 shows a plot of normalized output voltage versus spatial frequency. The response gradually drops off as more and more peaks are simultaneously placed under the skid. The dotted line shows the effect of edge bluntness. The cutoff frequency is reached when the effective width of this edge, the pressure relief zone, equals the wavelength. In the Telefunken player this zone is about 0.5 μm wide—hence the spatial resolution potentially is as good as in an optical player. In practice, wear is a serious problem; in the actual player the stylus is automatically repolished after every play.

The track spacing is 3.5 μm and, because only 8-in. discs are used, the playing time is limited to 10 min. Master discs are recorded by

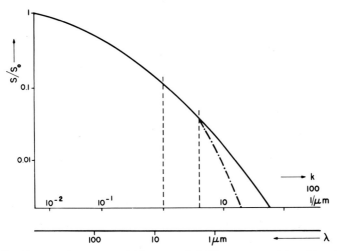

FIG. 9. Output voltage vs. spatial frequency in Teldec pressure pickup (From Dickopp and Redlich, 1973. Reprinted from *Electronics*. Copyright © 1973 by McGraw–Hill Book Company.)

mechanical cutting, in expanded time, and copies are made by embossing.

Consumer acceptance of the player in Germany has been very limited
and, at the time of writing, the market emphasis had shifted to insti-
tutional and educational applications.

The impact of the Teldec system on further video-disc development
has been consequential mainly in the application of flexible discs. Such
discs can be replicated easily—embossing is very much like printing—
and, as Teldec showed, their flying characteristics can be conveniently
stabilized by aerodynamic means. I will show later how the engineers
at Thomson–CSF perfected this stabilization to bring it within the
depth-of-focus of an optical player.

C. RCA

The next video-disc effort was launched by RCA (Clemens, 1976)
after this company had stopped further work on the holographic
videotape system (Hannan *et al.,* 1973) it had developed earlier.
Whereas the latter system had used the latest and most sophisticated
techniques available—such as holography, speckle reduction by redundancy, etc.—the video-disc player was deliberately kept simple.
No laser is used at all; instead a contacting stylus reads out the presence
of pits in a groove, by detecting capacitance variations. This is illustrated in Fig. 10.

When a pit passes under the stylus, the metal electrode senses a
capacitance variation of about 3.5×10^{-16} F. (This may seem very
small but with, say, 10 V across the capacitor, it still represents a
variation in charge of 2×10^4 electrons.) The capacitance change is
detected by energizing, at 915 MHz, a resonant circuit that includes
the capacitance between stylus and disc.

The disc-making process is fairly complicated. First, grooves are cut
in a master disc, which is subsequently coated with a sensitive emulsion. The pits encoding the video signal are recorded, on the bottom
of the grooves, by means of an electron beam. Copies are made by
standard pressing techniques; the thickness of the completed disc is
about the same as that of a conventional audio record. After pressing
the discs are coated with three layers of material: a metallic layer to
carry capacitive charge, a dielectric layer to provide insulation between
the first layer and an electrode on the stylus, and a layer of lubricant
to minimize wear.

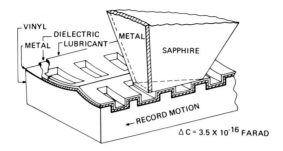

FIG. 10.   RCA capacitive pickup. (From Clemens, 1976.)

In contrast to most video discs, this one contains four complete TV frames per revolution and is spun at 450 rpm in playback. The track density equals 220/mm, the shortest recorded wavelength is 0.6 μm. Playing time of this 12-in. disc is ½hr per side but, at the time of writing, RCA had announced plans for a further increase to 1 hr per side. The life of the disc is said to be 500 plays, that of the sapphire stylus 500 hr.

It is interesting to note that, as in the Teldec player, the groove walls only provide the force needed for tracking correction; coarse tracking is effected by a mechanical arm linked to the turntable rotation. Of further interest is the provision of a so-called ''arm-stretcher'' servo system that corrects instantaneous speed variations by moving the stylus along the track.

The main attraction of the RCA player is its simplicity; disadvantages are stylus and disc wear and the absence of a fast random access capability. This, and the 4-frames/revolution format, makes the system less suitable for stop-frame and slow-motion effects.

D. PHILIPS–MCA

In the early 1970s, both Philips and MCA had started development of optical players using reflective, phase-relief-type discs (Compaan and Kramer, 1973, 1974; Broadbent, 1974; Winslow, 1976a,b). Because of the similarity of concepts, the two companies later on decided to make their players and discs compatible. As shown in Fig. 11 the basic optical system of the early Philips–MCA player consists of a He–Ne laser (2), a beam splitter (5), a photodiode (6), a mirror for radial tracking (4), and a microscope objective (3). The latter is mounted in

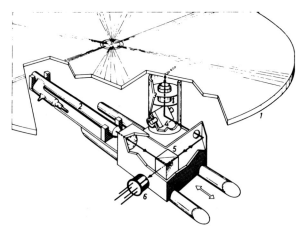

Fig. 11.   Philips optical pickup. (From Compaan and Kramer, 1973.)

a loudspeaker-type movement and can be moved up and down for focus tracking.

The disc is 1.1 mm thick and made of transparent plastic. One side is embossed with the information, covered with a thin layer of metal, and sealed with a protective coating. Readout is through the other side of the disc and fingerprints, scratches, etc., on that side are well out of focus and do not cause interference. The encoding is in the form of micropits arranged along a spiral track. When such a pit passes under the focused laser beam, it scatters the light, which, in turn, is detected by a photodiode as a momentary decrease of reflected light level.

The track density is 660/mm and the highest spatial frequency read-out is 1270/mm. The 12-in. disc rotates at 1800 rpm (U.S. version) or 1500 rpm (European version) and is recorded from an inner radius of 55 mm to an outer radius of 140 mm so as to provide $\frac{1}{2}$ hr of playing time.

Unique apsects of this player are the inclusion of a focus servo and the use of reflective discs. This latter feature is extremely important as it makes it possible to protect the information surface by sealing it with a scratch-resistant layer of plastic. Such a process is not possible with transmissive discs. The protective layer fills up the pits and since these, in a transmissive system, do not have reflective boundaries they become essentially invisible. Thus, in spite of the fact that transmissive discs are easier to produce and that they simplify the optical system—no return path is required—reflective discs are specified in the technical recommendations formulated by engineers from Philips, MCA, and Zenith (Boegels, 1976).

The same guidelines also recommend both thin (200 μm) and thick 1.1 mm) discs of 8- and 12-in. diam. It was realized that, although thick discs provide maximum protection and are best suited for expensive program material such as movies, plays, operas, etc., thin discs lend themselves best for mailing and insertion in magazines, which is convenient for news and sports programs, documentaries, and promotional material. Consequently, the latest version of the Philips–MCA player has provision for playing thin discs, in agreement with the technical recommendations.

E. THOMSON–CSF

During the same period that Philips and MCA were developing a reflective player, the French company Thomson–CSF had started work on a player for flexible transmissive discs (Broussaud *et al.*, 1974; Bricot *et al.*, 1976). In some respects this system was simpler than that of Philips. For one thing, it used a so-called aerodynamic stabilizer instead of a more complex focusing servo. The stabilizer arrangement is shown in Fig. 12. In operation, a flexible thin disc (150 μm thick) is spun at 1800 rpm above a set of smoothing planes and passes between the upper and lower surfaces of a U-shaped stabilizer. The gap between the surfaces is very narrow, of the order of 200 μm. When the disc flies through the gap at high speed, the entrained air, carried with it, is compressed and forms a springy cushion that stabilizes the flying of the disc. Initial flutter (without stabilizer) of 50–100 μm may be reduced by a factor of 25 with this system (Ahmed *et al.*, 1975).

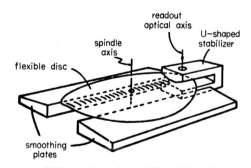

FIG. 12.   Thomson–CSF aerodynamic stabilizer. (From Bricot *et al.*, 1976.)

The drawback to this simple and ingenious device is that large dust particles occasionally pass through the gap and damage the disc. For laboratory experiments this is not too serious because clean air can usually be provided and also because, even in a normal room environment, damage does not happen too often. For consumer applications even a small likelihood of damage is, of course, intolerable and the latest version of this player uses a focus servo for that reason.

As discussed before, transmissive discs are easily damaged by careless handling. Fingerprints tend to fill up the pits and make them invisible, scratches damage the information surface and, if the discs are thin—as the Thomson system—they may be easily creased. At the time of writing, the Thomson discs are packed in an automatic cassette so that they are never touched by the user.

It should be pointed out that flexible transmissive discs are ideal for a laboratory environment where proper care can be exercised in handling. Of all discs, they can be produced quickest and with the least amount of processing.

F. HITACHI

All the systems discussed so far use time-sequential recording of information. The reader may have asked himself why holography (and, in particular, Fourier holography) has not been applied. Does it not, after all, offer the unique advantage of avoiding problems of tracking and focusing? This is, of course true, and at least one company, Hitachi, has experimented with such a system (Tsunoda *et al.*, 1976). As shown in Fig. 13, small holograms, of about 1 mm² area, are recorded on the disc in spiral fashion. As in the earlier RCA Holotape system (Hannan *et al.*, 1973) the holograms are illuminated with a relatively broad ($\approx$1-mm diam.) laser beam and the reconstructed image, in the Fourier transform plane, is scanned out with a vidicon. Color encoding in this system is similar to the technique pioneered by CBS in its EVR player (Goldmark, 1970); i.e., a separate image carries the color information and is scanned out with a second vidicon.

From an economic point of view the vidicons, necessary in holographic systems, are a liability. They are more complex, and certainly more expensive, than the simple photodiode used to read out linear recordings. Another drawback to holographic techniques is the difficulty of sound recording. The motion of the Hitachi disc is continuous

FIG. 13.   Small holograms recorded on Hitachi video disc. (From Tsunoda *et al.*, 1976.)

but too slow (3 rpm) for time-sequential sound recording. This problem is solved by recording segments of sound in the radial direction and fusing them very carefully upon playback so as not to cause audible interruption or overlap. In the Hitachi system the sound segments are stored as sequential radial holograms (a $\frac{1}{30}$-sec segment contains 110 holograms of 144 bits each) and recorded on an auxiliary track. This is shown in Fig. 14. From a technological point of view this is an exciting technique but, again, the economic disadvantages, relative to sequential recording, are obvious.

Finally the various kinds of speckle noise, inherent in holography, require special recording techniques. RCA, in its Holotape technique, made use of redundancy by recording many identical subholograms. The price paid is an increased information area per picture (≈ 54 mm^2). Hitachi makes small holograms (≈ 1 mm^2) by means of a random-phase sampling method (Tsunoda and Takeda, 1974). It is claimed that, with this method, redundancy is achieved without sacrifice of recording area.

Because of their complexity, it does not appear likely that holographic systems will evolve into consumer products, ingenious as they may be. In the rest of the article I will therefore concentrate on methods of time-sequential recording.

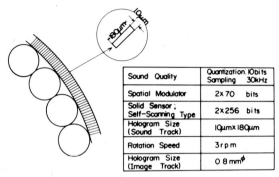

Sound Quality	Quantization: 10bits Sampling 30kHz
Spatial Modulator	2x70 bits
Solid Sensor ; Self-Scanning Type	2x256 bits
Hologram Size (Sound Track)	10μmx180μm
Rotation Speed	3 rpm
Hologram Size (Image Track)	0 8 mm⁺

FIG. 14. Sound hologram recorded on Hitachi video disc. (From Tsunoda *et al.*, 1976.)

G. I/O METRICS

The I/O Metrics concept differs from the ones described so far in that it proposes to use a multilayer photographic record to be read out by an incandescent lamp rather than a laser (Kaczorowski and Jerome, 1974). The tracks are spaced rather further apart ($\simeq 5$ μm) than in most other systems. It is claimed that this minimizes cost and complexity of tracking and focus servos and that it allows the use of an incandescent lamp. In order to obtain sufficient playing time, several layers of recorded information are to be laminated together; selection of each particular layer is by focusing. It is said that diazo contact prints can be produced by a relatively simple process. At the time of writing no technical details have been revealed nor have plans for marketing the player been announced.

IV. Encoding

Although it is possible to linearize the response of the photoresist medium used for mastering (Bartolini, 1974), this requires great care and also limits the exposure levels that can be used. It is therefore common practice to, instead, exploit the nonlinear properties of the photoresist by using a two-level recording technique. Thus the developed master will exhibit rectangular indentations or pits and so will the pressed record. By using negative photoresist it is possible to record "bumps" rather than pits. Optically there is not much difference (bumps scatter as well as pits), but the small localized areas of negative photoresist that remain after development are more vulnerable to damage and become detached rather easily.

The two-level process is also well suited to recording media other than photoresist. MCA, in its earlier experiments (Winslow, 1976a, b) used a glass master plate coated with a thin layer of metal. The information was recorded by melting small holes in the metal; the master could then be read out immediately, which offered the possibility of almost instantaneous exposure control. Philips has recently announced a similar system for computer use (*Electronics,* June 9, 1977).

Two-level encoding is very familiar to electrical engineers; it is generally called pulse coding and many variants exist. One may vary the frequency of the pulses, (FM or frequency modulation) their width (width or duty cycle modulation), their position (pulse position modulation), or their sequence (pulse code modulation, delta modulation, etc.) (Lathi, 1968). The two first techniques are examples of analog encoding, the two latter ones are digital. It is somewhat confusing to use the term analog encoding when pulses are used in the process, but what is meant is that each pulse is an analog sample. It carries information about the original continuous signal by an analog change of its timing parameters. Thus the times of occurrence of the leading and trailing edges of the pulse may specify two independent analog values, or the time of occurrence of the pulse center may encode one value and the width of the pulse another one. In general then, each pulse can carry two independent samples, although these may be encoded in different ways.

In most video-disc formats the video (color and luminance) is encoded as frequency modulation, i.e., by the duration of the pulse repetition period. The sound is encoded by a modulation of the duty cycle, i.e., by varying the ratio between the pulse duration and the pulse repetition period. Figure 15a illustrates an unmodulated pulse train (with 50% duty cycle), in Fig. 15b frequency modulation only is applied, and Fig. 15c shows pure duty-cycle modulation.

The frequency allocations proposed in the Philips–MCA–Zenith recommendations are shown in Fig. 16. As mentioned before, the video-signal frequency modulates a pulse train located at the nominal frequency of 8 MHz. More specifically, 8 MHz corresponds to the black portions of the picture, 9.2 MHz to the white portions, and 7.5 MHz to the tips of the synchronization signals. The total frequency deviation is thus 1.7 MHz. As indicated by the large triangles, the modulation

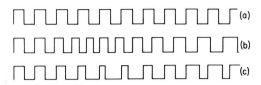

FIG. 15.   (a) Unmodulated pulse train; (b) frequency modulated; (c) duty-cycle modulated.

sidebands of the luminance extend about 4.5 MHz from peak white (i.e., to 13.7 MHz) and downward from black (i.e., to 3.5 MHz). The sidebands generated by the chroma subcarriers are indicated by the small triangles. Two FM audio subcarriers are used, at 2.3 MHz and at 2.8 MHz; they are duty-cycle modulated on the main pulse carrier.

As far as the requirements for optical readout are concerned, it has been found that a temporal cutoff frequency of 13.2 MHz is sufficient. At the inner disc radius of 55 mm the tangential velocity is 10.4 m/sec and hence the temporal cutoff frequency of 13.2 MHz corresponds to a spatial cutoff frequency of 1270 cycles/mm. Using a He–Ne laser, such a cutoff frequency is achieved using a lens with NA = 0.4.

I shall not discuss the technical details of the electronics involved in the encoding and decoding; they are fairly standard and not of much interest to optical engineers.

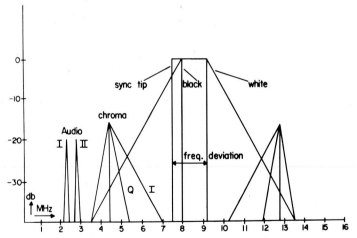

FIG. 16.   Video-disc frequency allocations in the MCA–Phillips–Zenith recommendations.

In addition to the frequency response, one other aspect of the encoding is of great importance to the optics of the system, (specifically to mastering): the requirement that the average duty cycle of the FM carrier be between 40 and 60%. If these limits are exceeded, excessive intermodulation products of the various subcarriers and main carrier will be generated, and these show up in the image. This places strict requirements on disc mastering as we will discuss in the next section.

V. Mastering and Replication

Figure 17 shows a diagram of the optical mastering system we have used at Zenith (Palermo *et al.*, 1977). The master disc is a ¼-in. thick Pyrex plate to which a thin layer of photoresist has been applied by a spin-coating process. A 100-mW He–Cd laser is used for recording; modulation is effected by a Pockels-type electrooptic modulator. An acoustooptic modulator is used to equalize the exposure levels for different disc radii. To that purpose a so-called taper signal, proportional to the recording radius, controls the exposure level by varying the amount of diffracted light. The undiffracted light is used for recording. A beam splitter diverts part of the incident light for signal monitoring, and part of the reflected light for focus monitoring. The output of photodiode No. 2 is maximum when the disc is in focus and all the reflected light returns through the pinhole spatial filter located in the focal plane of the intermediate lens. Any deviation from focus will result in part

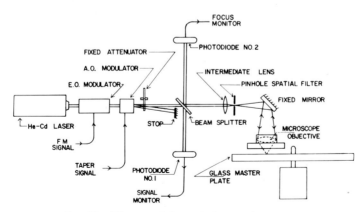

FIG. 17. Diagram of the optical mastering system.

of the reflected light being intercepted by the spatial filter and will be noticed as a decrease in the photodiode current. Although the resulting electrical signal is not bipolar and cannot be used for servoing purposes, it is nevertheless very convenient for initial focus adjustment and for making slight corrections during recording. The actual dynamic focus control is accomplished by an air bearing of the SRI type, discussed in Section II.

The (underfilled) microscope objective has a numerical aperture of 0.75 and projects a roughly Gaussian spot with 0.5-μm diam ($1/e^2$ intensity points) on the disc. The spatial frequency at which the response is down to $1/e^2$ is 2500 cycles/mm. The photoresist itself is capable of recording up to about 2000 cycles/mm (Bartolini, 1974). Both limiting spatial frequencies are well above the 1270 cycles/mm required for recording the spectrum of Fig. 16.

As said before, it is necessary that the nominal duty cycle of the recorded sequence of pits be between 40 and 60%. To stay within this tolerance it is necessary to accurately control both the exposure and the development. We have chosen to fix the development time at 40 sec; the proper exposure is determined by making a test disc using a range of light levels with each level corresponding to a recording band. The quality of playback serves as a criterion for selecting the desired band. A somewhat more convenient way is to monitor the light diffracted by the disc as it is being developed and to stop development at a level of diffraction previously correlated with a 50% duty cycle (Beesley and Castledine, 1970).

Figure 18 is a photograph of our optical video-disc recorder. Note the heavy turntable; it is controlled by a tachometer in conjunction with a master crystal reference at twice the chroma subcarrier frequency of approximately 3.6 MHz.

After development, the photoresist layer on the master plate is provided with a thin nickel coating by a process of electroless deposition. Electroplating then builds up this initial layer to a thickness of 0.2–0.3 mm. Upon removal of the layer, some further cleaning, and suitable mounting, it may be used as a stamper for embossing thin sheets or as part of a mold in the compression- or injection-molding process for thick discs. Alternatively it may be preserved as a master negative from which additional metal copies can be made.

At Zenith we have concentrated on the embossing technique as it is easier to implement than a molding process. Figure 19 shows the relatively simple book-type press which we use. It operates at a pres-

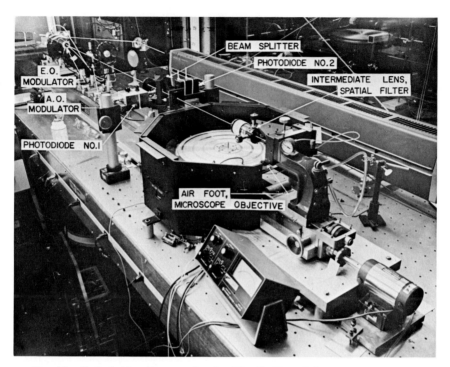

Fig. 18.   Optical video-disc recorder after Fig. 17. (From Palermo *et al.*, 1977. Courtesy Zenith Radio Corp. Reprinted with permission of IPC Science and Technology Press Ltd., Guildford, Surrey, United Kingdom.)

sure of 6–9 atm at a temperature of about 280°F. The disc material is nonplasticized PVC (polyvinyl chloride), which is readily available in sheet form. Figure 20 is micrograph of the pit structure on the finished disc, taken with a scanning electron-beam microscope. The length of the pits is approximately 12 μm; track separation is 2.5 μm.

VI. Readout

A. One-Half Wavelength Pits

In principle reading out a pitted disc is very simple: whenever a pit passes under the focused laser beam, part of the light is scattered out of the receiving aperture and this, in turn, manifests itself by a decrease

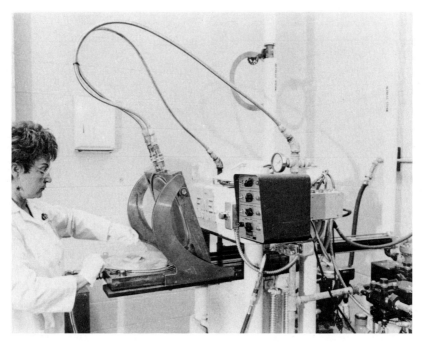

FIG. 19. Embossing of flexible video discs. (From Palermo *et al.*, 1977; Courtesy Zenith Radio Corp. Reprinted with permission of IPC Science and Technology Press Ltd., Guildford, Surrey, United Kingdom.)

in current from a photodiode placed in the receiver plane. The photodiode is usually located somewhere in the far field of the focused spot, although sometimes it is set in an image plane of the readout spot (and hence of the pit). As scattering is the predominant signal-generating mechanism—no photons are lost by absorption as in a photographic recording—it is necessary to limit the receiving aperture in order to obtain a signal. In a reflective system this is automatically taken care of by the finite aperture of the focusing microscope objective. In a transmissive system the photodiode is located at that plane in the far field where the unperturbed diverging cone of light emanating from the focus just fills the diode aperture. Any scattered light then falls outside the diode and reduces its output.

For most effective scattering it is necessary that: (a) there be one-half wavelength difference in optical pathlength between rays going through the center of the pit and rays traversing the surrounding land area and (b) half of the total area of the focused spot be intercepted by the pit. This situation is depicted in Fig. 21, which also shows the resulting rf signal, i.e., the time-varying reduction of the average current when the track moves through the focused beam (Korpel, 1977). It is easy to convince oneself that under conditions (a) and (b) there exists a zero in the far field of the scattered beam—an indication of strong scattering—when the latter is incident on the center of the pit. For a transmissive system the depth of the pit h must be chosen such that

$$h = \tfrac{1}{2}[\lambda/(n - 1)] \tag{1}$$

where λ is the wavelength in air and n is the refractive index of the

FIG. 20. Electron micrograph of pit structure on video disc. The length of the pits is approximately 1.2 μm; track separation is 2.5 μm. (From Palermo *et al.*, 1977; Courtesy Zenith Radio Corp. Reprinted with permission of IPC Science and Technology Press Ltd., Guildford, Surrey, United Kingdom.)

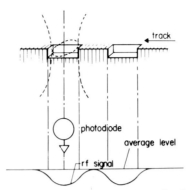

FIG. 21.   The rf signal derived from radial scattering by a $\frac{1}{2}\lambda$ pit. (From Korpel, 1977.)

disc material. For plastics such as PVC, of which discs are usually made, $n \simeq 1.5$ and hence, with $\lambda = 6328$ Å, the pit depth must be of the order of 6000 Å for maximum scattering. In a reflective system, where the pathlength is automatically doubled, the depth of the pit is simply made equal to one-quarter of the wavelength in the plastic if the readout is through the disc thickness and one-quarter of the wavelength in air otherwise. Thus, reflective discs usually have shallower pits (1000–1500 Å) than transmissive ones.

Simple scattering calculations of video-disc readout commonly make use of a simple ray picture in the waist area of the focused beam. All rays are assumed to traverse the pit area in parallel formation and one simply calculates the individual phase delay for each ray. From the resulting phase corrugation of the existing wavefront the far field is calculated. Knowing the geometry of the photodiode, it is then sim-ple—but cumbersome—to calculate the diode current. A rough indi-cation of scattering efficiency may be obtained faster by assuming the photodiode to be a point receiver located on the optical axis in the far field. In that case all that is needed is to calculate the square of the integrated amplitude of the phase-corrugated beam after it has trav-ersed the pit. The results of such a calculation are shown in Fig. 22 for the one-dimensional case of a rectangular beam incident on a re-flective rectangular pit. It is seen that maximum scattering obtains when conditions (a) and (b), discussed before, are satisfied. Note also that the scattering behavior is periodic with pit depth, i.e., it makes no difference whether the differential phase delay is π, 3π, 5π, etc. Be-cause of the rather crude ray picture used, not too much emphasis should be placed on this aspect. [The same theory predicts no scattering at all for phase differentials of $m \times 2\pi$ (m is an integer) no matter how large m—and hence the depth of the pit—really is. Yet it seems intuitively obvious that deep pits will scatter a lot of light regardless of their exact depth.]

It is not the intention to discuss very deeply the detailed theoretical aspects of light scattering in this article, but it is useful for the reader to realize how simple a model may be used in calculating video-disc performance. As long as the pits are shallow, the model is probably reasonably good, but not too much significance should be attached to quantitative results.

Although we have not found it too difficult to record rectangular pits with our mastering process (see Fig, 20), there exist other, potentially

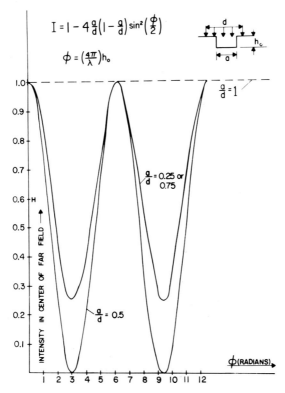

FIG. 22.   On-axis intensity in far field vs. scattering depth of a rectangular pit illuminated by a rectangular beam.

useful, ways of mastering that result in different pit shapes and also appear to work well. In fact, the early process used by MCA (Winslow, 1976a, b) resulted in rather tall (≈ 1 µm) bumps rather than pits. On the basis of the simple model discussed above, there is no difference in scattering behavior between convex and concave surfaces and intuitively, too, there seems to be no reason why one should scatter better than the other. It is not immediately clear however what the depth of a nonrectangular pit profile should be for optimum scattering. To gain some insight into this we have, at Zenith, applied the ray model to a one-dimensional Gaussian pit profile illuminated by a Gaussian beam. The results are shown in Fig. 23. Note that optimum scattering occurs for a peak differential phase delay of 4.5 rad, as compared to 3.1 rad for the rectangular pit. It is evident from Fig. 23 that, in spite of a weak periodic behavior—which may be an artifact due to our crude

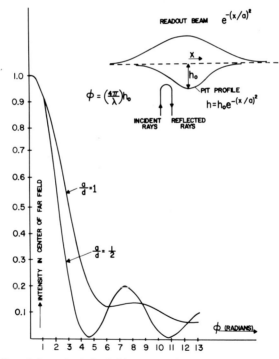

FIG. 23.   On-axis intensity in far field vs. scattering depth of a Gaussian pit illuminated by a Gaussian beam.

model—the scattering asymptotically approaches the maximum level when the pit gets deeper. It thus appears that, for nonrectangular cross sections, the depth of the pit may not be very critical; a certain minimum depth is required, rather than an optimum depth. If this is true (not enough experimental evidence exists at the present time), it would relax tolerances and broaden the range of disc-making methods.

The MTF of a "$\frac{1}{2}\lambda$" phase-relief pit system is not much different from one using, say, photographic discs. A phase shift of one-half wavelength is equivalent to a multiplication of the amplitude by minus one, and thus a "$\frac{1}{2}\lambda$" phase-relief disc is like an amplitude object, in a somewhat broader sense. The results of a much simplified calculation for rectangular pits are shown in Fig. 24 for various conditions of focus. A uniformly illuminated square lens aperture is assumed, d is the half-width of the focused spot (center to first zero), and h is the out-of-focus distance. The width of the rectangular pits b is taken to be half the width of the focused spot, for optimum scattering. The linear sequence of pits used in the model has a 50% duty cycle; the spatial period is denoted by $2a$. For ease of calculations the sinc X sinc Y distribution of the focused spot has been replaced by an equivalent square area of size $d \times d$. A (square) photodiode is assumed to be located in the far field; it is just large enough to intercept all the light in the unperturbed beam. The ordinate in the figure represents the relative amplitude of the fundamental harmonic component in the current from the photodiode; the abscissa denotes the spatial frequency relative to the cutoff frequency ($1/d$) of the lens. Note that the first zero in the MTF occurs when the pits are out of focus by a distance given by the well-known expression $h = 4d^2/\lambda = \lambda/(NA)^2$. For actual conditions of operation ($\lambda = 6328$ Å, NA = 0.4) this implies a total focus tolerance of about 4 μm. Although the model used in the calculations is extremely simple, actual measurements are in fair agreement with the results shown in Fig. 24.

The MTF of the system does not give a complete picture of its performance. It is, in fact, rather misleading because it tends to obscure the fact that phase-relief detection is basically nonlinear and certainly so when rectangular pits of considerable phase depth are involved. This is easily realized by recognizing that even a sinusoidal phase grating exhibits multiple orders in diffraction; when read out by a scanning beam such orders manifest themselves by the presence of higher harmonics in the signal from the photodetector. In turn, such harmonics distort the wave shape of the signal and introduce uncertainties in the

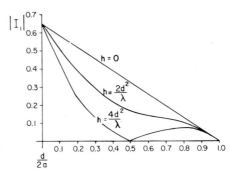

FIG. 24.   Approximate MTF applying to a $\frac{1}{2}\lambda$ recording, for various conditions of focus.

detection of the leading and trailing edges that correspond to the beginning and end of the pits. As we have seen in Section IV, such uncertainties in the location of "zero crossings" may introduce spurious signals in the final image. If we now look at the wave shape shown in Fig. 21, we begin to realize the difficulty of locating the zero crossings and also how much this location depends on factors such as the shape of the beam, the shape of the pit edge, etc. In spite of these difficulties the system can be made to work remarkably well in practice; all the same it should be kept in mind that the basic scattering mechanism indicates the center of the pits and that the location of edges is derived indirectly and requires care in alignment. A simpler system would detect edges directly, for instance by deflection of the beam—in different directions for leading and trailing edges—rather than by scattering. It turns out that this is possible by making the pits such that the differential phase delay equals one-quarter wavelength instead of one-half wavelength. Such a "$\frac{1}{4}\lambda$" system was developed both by Zenith (Korpel, 1976) and by Thomson–CSF; we will discuss it in the next section.

B. One-Quarter Wavelength Pits

In this mode of operation the diameter of the focused spot need not be larger than the width of the pit, because radial scattering is not essential to the detection process. Rather the beam is deflected tangentially when the edge of the pit passes under it, How this comes about is shown in Fig. 25a. After traversing the region near the edge, the wavefronts in the left half of the beam are displaced by $\frac{1}{4}\lambda$ with respect to those in the right half. The thin, sloping lines represent the nominal wavefronts of the emerging beam which is seen to be deflected to the left, as indicated by the arrow. It is easy to convince oneself that the next (trailing) edge passing through will deflect the beam to the right. Consequently, a split photodiode, connected in push–pull as indicated in the drawing, will deliver positive and negative pulses whose occurrence coincides with the edges of the pits. As indicated in Fig. 25b, such a system will not work with $\frac{1}{2}\lambda$ pits; the same construction as before now results in two nominal wavefronts making equal and opposite angles with the optical axis. This is an indication of symmetrical tangential scattering rather than deflection of symmetrical tan-

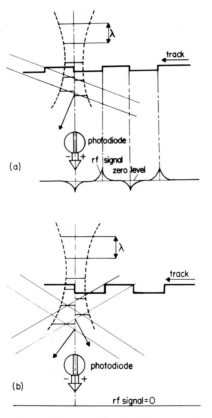

FIG. 25.   (a) Asymmetric scattering of $\frac{1}{4}\lambda$ pits; (b) symmetric scattering of $\frac{1}{2}\lambda$ pits. (From Korpel, 1977.)

gential scattering rather than deflection; the light intensities on the two halves of the photodiode are equal and no net signal results (Adler, 1974; Korpel, 1974a, b; Whitman, 1974).

It should be noted that in principle any differential phase delay other than $\frac{1}{2}\lambda$ causes some deflection of the beam. Optimum operation is obtained at $\frac{1}{4}\lambda$ or, more precisely, at $\frac{1}{4}\lambda$, $\frac{3}{4}\lambda$, etc., because, at least in theory, the same kind of periodicity exists that we have noticed before in the $\frac{1}{2}\lambda$ case. However, as before, this predicted periodic behavior should not be taken too seriously as the theory may not be valid for deeper pits. The available experimental data only indicate that $\frac{1}{4}\lambda$ works well and $\frac{1}{2}\lambda$ does not.

Figure 26 shows the calculated MTF of a $\frac{1}{4}\lambda$ phase-relief pit system with push–pull detection. The same assumptions were made as used to calculate the MTF of Fig. 24. The photodiode was assumed to be infinite in extent with the split between the two halves perpendicular to the track and on the optical axis of the system. The triangular form of the MTF is typical for slope-detection systems: for low spatial frequencies of constant amplitude the slope decreases and so does the photodiode current. For high spatial frequencies the current decreases too, this time because the limiting resolution is reached. An optimum occurs when the diameter (d) of the focused spot equals the pit length (a).

As pointed out earlier, the MTF gives no indication about the inherent nonlinearities in the system or about the accuracy in detecting zero crossings. Because the $\frac{1}{4}\lambda$ technique gives more direct indication of pit edges than the $\frac{1}{2}\lambda$ system, it is theoretically more distortion free. This is confirmed in practice: the optical parameters are less critical

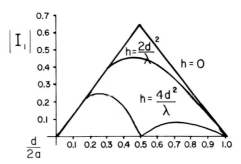

FIG. 26.   Approximate MFT applying to a $\frac{1}{4}\lambda$ recording, for various conditions of focus.

and somewhat more pit distortion can be tolerated. A rather high price has to be paid for this in practice, though, in that no compatibility exists with potential methods of disc-making that can use less well-controlled scattering—using ground-glass-type areas rather than pits would be an example—or with photographic discs (Michael and McFee, 1973). In view of this, the recommendations proposed by Philips–MCA–Zenith specify a $\frac{1}{2}\lambda$-pit format or any other format compatible with it.

VII. Radial Tracking

For radial tracking the beam is steered by a galvanometric mirror. At Zenith we have used the two-axis mirror shown in Fig. 27 (Wossidlo, 1976); rotation about one of the axes moves the beam across the track, the other axis is used for tangential tracking. The mirror itself is mounted on a small permanent magnet which pivots on a pin and is held in place by another ring-type permanent magnet underneath it. Four orthogonal coils act, in pairs, on the stray field of the mirror magnet, thus providing independent motion in two directions.

The tracking error signal needed to actuate the mirror is easily obtained in a $\frac{1}{4}\lambda$ system. The principle of operation, shown in Fig. 28, is similar to that used in reading out the pit edges (Hrbek, 1974). In addition to the pair of diodes for rf readout, a second pair is used but this time with the split between dc diodes parallel to the track rather than perpendicular to it. (In actual practice a four-segment diode is used combining both rf and track-error readout). The differential phase shift caused by the track edge causes the beam to be deflected either to the inside or the outside of the record, depending on the displacement of the focused beam relative to the trace. Thus a bipolar error signal is obtained which, after further electronic processing, is fed to the galvanometric mirror.

In a $\frac{1}{2}\lambda$ system such a simple scheme is no longer possible; as we have seen before, in this case the beam is scattered symmetrically rather then deflected. Philips has used a technique with two auxiliary focused beams to derive a tracking signal for $\frac{1}{2}\lambda$ records. This is shown in Fig. 29 (Bouwhuis and Burgstede, 1973). A special phase grating G splits the incident beam into three orders. The zero order is used for readout, the other two for tracking. By proper alignment of the phase grating the latter two orders form spots on the records that are slightly displaced radially in opposite directions relative to the main readout

FIG. 27. Two-axis tracking mirror. (Courtesy Zenith Radio Corp.)

spot. Three separate photodiodes are placed in a reflected image plane of the record. The difference in dc current from the two outer diodes gives a bipolar indication of beam position.

Although this technique works well, it requires care in the alignment of the grating and the photodiodes. A simpler system is the so-called "spot-wobble" technique, shown in Fig. 30 (Bricot *et al.*, 1976). Here the focused beam is wobbled, at a rate of some 50 kHz, across the track. The amount of wobble—much exaggerated in the picture—is very small, of the order of tenths of microns. The dc current from the rf photodiode contains a component of 50 kHz which disappears when

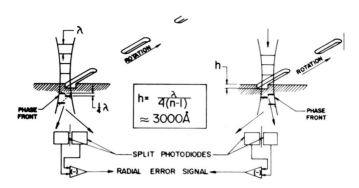

FIG. 28. Radial tracking signal derived from asymmetric scattering of $\frac{1}{4}\lambda$ pits. (From Hrbek, 1974. Copyright © 1974 by the Society of Motion Picture and Television Engineers, Inc., Scarsdale, New York. Reprinted with permission.)

the beam is exactly on the center of the track. (It is readily seen that the change in scattering caused by the wobble is then just as large whether the beam moves radially in or out and hence only the second harmonic of 50 kHz is generated.) The phase of the photodiode signal, with respect to the phase of the wobble, gives an indication whether the focused beam is off-center to the inside or the outside. In the figure the main galvanometric tracking mirror is made to oscillate weakly at

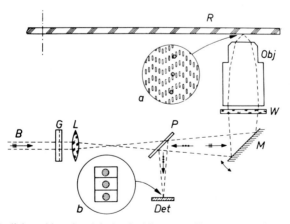

FIG. 29. Radial tracking signal derived with two auxiliary beams in $\frac{1}{2}\lambda$ system. (From Bouwhuis and Burgstede, 1973, 1974.)

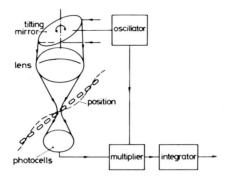

FIG. 30.   Radial tracking signal derived with spot wobble. (From Bricot *et al.*, 1976.)

the wobble frequency. A phase detector (multiplier) compares the phase of the driving signal with the 50-kHz signal from the photodiode. The dc output of the phase detector is, after further electronic processing, fed back to the tracking mirror, which now corrects the beam position.

Instead of wobbling the main tracking mirror, one can of course use an auxiliary mirror for that purpose. At Zenith we have experimented with an in-line wobbler shown in Fig. 31 (Adler, 1976a, b). A small, thin block of glass is excited in an ultrasonic flexure mode by the transducer visible on top. The resulting changes in stress inside the glass give rise to refractive index variations which periodically deflect a traversing laser beam. This acoustic–optic wobbler works well, but great care must be taken in mounting it so as not to damp its acoustic resonance.

VIII. Tangential Tracking

As pointed out before, speed variations in the record will interfere with the correct timing of synchronization signals as well as with the proper phase of the color subcarrier. Television receivers in the United States generally have large time constants in their synchronization and color demodulation circuits, for reasons of noise suppression. Hence, such receivers cannot follow the fast variations caused by speed fluctuations. A typical example of faulty synchronization is shown in Fig. 32 (Hrbek, 1974). For sake of clarity the start of the beam scan has

FIG. 31.   Elastooptic in-line spot wobbler. (After Adler, 1976a; Courtesy Zenith Radio Corp.)

been located in the center of the screen for this experiment. The screen on the left shows a video-disc picture without tangential-tracking compensation; the one on the right shows the result of activating the servo loop.

The error signal for the tracking mirror is obtained by measuring the frequency of the synchronization pulses read off the disc, for instance with a frequency discriminator. (In the experiment of Fig. 32 a special pilot carrier was actually used.) This is sufficient for the correction of timing errors but not for the correction of phase errors of the color subcarrier. As mentioned in Section II, the phase of this carrier encodes the hue or shade of the color. To avoid noticeable changes in hue, phase variations must be kept to within $10°$ (Fink, 1975); for a subcarrier frequency of 3.58 MHz, this implies a timing error of less than 8×10^{-9} sec, a factor of 10 smaller than the error allowed in the timing of the

Fɪɢ. 32.   Faulty synchronization due to speed variations (left); corrected by tangential-tracking servo (right). (From Hrbek, 1974. Copyright © 1974 by the Society of Motion Picture and Television Engineers, Inc., Scarsdale, New York. Reprinted with permission.)

synchronization pulses. In order to correct such small variations, it is necessary to derive an error signal by measuring not only the frequency but also the phase of the synchronization pulses read off the disc. I will not discuss the details of such a double servo loop; suffice it to say that, in spite of its electronic complexity and its very simple mechanics, it can be made to work surprisingly well.

Although the electromechanical servo mirror is quite effective it should not be thought that it is the only way to correct the effect of speed variations. A much easier method is to change the time constants in the TV set and, in the laboratory, we have done this routinely for ease of experimentation. In practice, however, changing the time constants does not offer a viable solution in view of the millions of sets, already in people's homes, that would have to be modified.

Another method of timing correction is by means of electronically variable delay lines. Such lines are rapidly becoming practical with the technology of charge-coupled devices (CCDs). It is to be expected that they will eventually be used for tangential correction in video-disc players, thereby eliminating one of the two tracking-mirror functions.

IX.   Focus Tracking

A video disc, rotating freely at 1800 rpm, exhibits more vertical wobble than can be corrected conveniently by a focus servo. Therefore a prestabilization system is necessary. Philips uses a fixed plate with a central hole, located close to the rotating disc; the rotating layer of air between disc and plate acts as a damped air bearing. At Zenith we have used a turntable with sharp concentric ridges. Due to the rapid spinning, the air between the ridges is expelled, thereby creating an underpressure that clamps the disc firmly to the turntable. An additional benefit with this system is that any wrinkles in thin flexible discs tend to be "ironed" out.

With both systems the residual flutter of the disc is of the order of ± 1 mm at 30 Hz and it decreases according to a $1/f^2$ law to reach ± 1 μm at about 1 kHz. As ± 1 μm is of the order of the depth of focus, it follows that the necessary servo gain must be about a factor 1000 (60 DB) at 30 Hz, decreasing to unity near 1 kHz.

To accomplish vertical tracking the microscope objective is mounted in a loudspeaker-type movement, as shown in Fig. 33 for the Philips system (Janssen and Day, 1973). In this drawing R_1 and R_2 are springs which suspend the objective, C is a coil, and M a permanent magnet. The flange E, near the exit pupil, was originally used to measure capacitance between itself and the metallized layer on the record. The value of this capacitance is a measure of the relative distance between lens and disc; it is compared with a desired value and the difference used to generate an error signal for the focus servo. Because the value of the capacitance is only indirectly related to optical pathlength, such a scheme cannot compensate perfectly for thickness variations in the disc. It has therefore been abandoned in favor of optical methods, some of which we will now discuss.

The method initially used in the Philips system (Compaan and Kramer, 1974) is shown in Fig. 34. It makes use of a separate beam 1, focused obliquely by the readout objective 6, to form a relatively large spot, covering many tracks, on the record. On its way to the record,

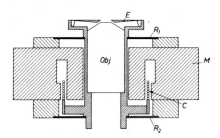

Fig. 33.   Servomotor for focus tracking. (From Janssen and Day, 1973.)

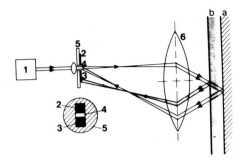

FIG. 34. Oblique-beam technique for deriving a focus-error signal. (From Compaan and Kramer, 1974.)

the beam passes through slit 4, between photodiodes 2 and 3. After reflection, the beam returns through slit 4 if the record is in focus. If the record is out of focus, the reflected beam hits either diode 2 or 3, depending on which side of focus the record happens to be. Thus the difference between photocurrents of diodes 2 and 3 constitutes a bipolar focus-error signal which, after further electronic processing, is fed back to the focus motor.

A system not requiring a separate beam was developed at Thomson–CSF (Bricot *et al.*, 1976). The principle of operation is shown in Figs. 35a and b. In Fig. 35a, the incident beam, originating from intermediate focus S, passes through a beam splitter M, and is focused by lens L on point S'—the image of S—on the record. After reflection the beam passes through cylinder lens Λ. Without the cylinder lens the beam would have been focused at A, the image of S. The cylinder lens astigmatizes the beam so as to form two orthogonal line foci: a vertical one at B and a horizontal one at the original position A. In a plane P_3, located halfway between A and B, the cross section of the beam is circular. In this plane is located a four-quadrant photodiode, with the separate segments connected as indicated in the left diagram of Fig. 35b. It is readily seen that the resulting photocurrent unbalance is zero. If the disc now goes out of focus, for instance by moving down, then the astigmatic foci move toward lens Λ (Fig. 35a). Consequently, the spot on the photodiodes takes on the character of the line focus at A: it becomes elongated horizontally. As indicated by the middle diagram of Fig. 35b, the output of the sensor system becomes positive. It is readily seen that a negative signal results when the disc moves upward out of focus; the spot on the photodiodes is shown by the right-hand

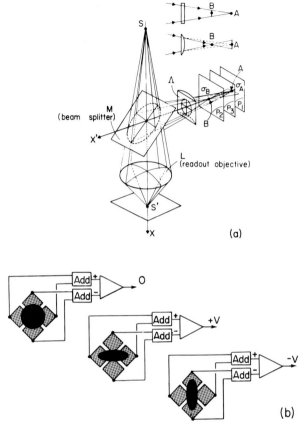

FIG. 35. (a) Astigmatic beam technique for deriving a focus-error signal; (b) sensor configuration in plane P_3. (From Bricot *et al.*, 1976.)

diagram in Fig. 35b. Hence this system, like the Philips technique, also results in a bipolar focus-error signal. It is, however, easier to implement because no separate beam is required.

An even simpler system, also developed by Thomson–CSF (Bricot *et al.*, 1976), is shown in Fig. 36. Here a small mask is placed in the edge of the return beam. When the disc is not in focus, the shadow of this mask falls on diode A or B, depending upon the out-of-focus direction. The difference between photodiode currents forms the error signal for the servo. The advantage of the asymmetric sensor over the

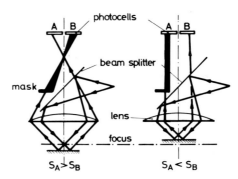

FIG. 36.   Asymmetric mask technique for deriving a focus-error signal. (From Bricot et al., 1976).

astigmatic sensor is its wider acquisition range (± 200 μm as compared to ± 50 μm). In cases where the low-frequency disc flutter is not too large, e.g., in flying thin flexible discs over a stabilizing plate, the asymmetric sensor makes it unnecessary to use a search mechanism (coarse acquisition) for finding the initial disc position.

All of the systems just discussed work in reflection, and it may have occurred to the reader that a different technique has to be developed for a transmissive system. Although such techniques have been investigated—one of them (unpublished) relies on measuring the phase difference of the rf carrier between the two halves of the split photodiode—they are relatively complicated and unreliable. Fortunately, it turns out that even the small reflection ($\simeq 4\%$) of a transmissive disc is sufficient to use the techniques developed for reflective discs.

X. Final Note

In the preceding sections I have discussed the main elements of current video-disc technology. This section will deal with some likely future developments and applications.

With regards to technical developments, it appears now very probable that, in two to four years, diode lasers will be commercially available at a price substantially lower than that of the He–Ne lasers currently used in most optical players. Such diode lasers offer many other advantages in addition: they are compact, light, and need only a very simple power supply. It is true though that their wavelength is larger

(8200 Å) than that of the He–Ne laser (6328 Å), so that a larger NA will have to be used (e.g., 0.52 instead of 0.40) for the same resolution. Efforts are currently underway however, to decrease the wavelength (Kressel *et al.*, 1977); even if not successful, the price to pay for a better lens may well be offset by the other advantages.

One such advantage is the possibility of making the optical layout very compact, thereby reducing the effect of vibrations and simplifying the alignment. Figure 37 shows a laser-diode reading head for transmissive discs we developed at Zenith. It uses a Hitachi buried heterostructure laser (Takeda and Tsunoda, 1977) that is mounted on a copper heatsink of about 1 cm³. In the figure this heatsink can be seen to the left of the horizontal adjusting screw. A small collimating lens, a tracking mirror, and a focusing lens complete the optical configuration. The diode laser delivers about 500 μW of infrared light (≈8200 Å) from

FIG. 37.   Optical reading head with laser diode. (Courtesy Zenith Radio Corp. and Hitachi.)

each of its facets. The light, which is essentially single mode, originates from a small aperture of 1.0×0.2 μm; the device constitutes a quasi-point source. Power requirements are very simple: 15 mA at 1.5 V. Hitachi has incorporated a similar diode in an optical reading head for reflective discs (Tsunoda *et al.*, 1977).

A further point of interest is that it may be possible to operate laser diodes in a feedback configuration, where the light reflected off the disc reenters the diode. The signal on the disc is then detected as a change in current through the diode or as a change in light flux emerging from the other facet (Morikawa *et al.*, 1976). Such an arrangement would obviously simplify the optics even more.

With regard to further applications of the optical video-disc player, the possibility of interactive viewing should be mentioned (Kenney, 1976; Mathieu, 1977). This comes about as a result of the random access capability of an optical player. Figure 38 illustrates that point for the Philips machine where information on the disc is read from the inside to the outside. (Compaan and Kramer, 1974). In Fig. 38a the laser beam is flipped back one trackspacing after each revolution, thus repeating the same picture over and over again. This "freeze-frame" mode of operation makes it possible to store approximately 50,000 separate "television pages" on each disc. With digital address codes in the picture, random access is obtained to any of these pages in a time of 5–10 sec. (Mathieu, 1977). The implications for teaching are evident; such a use may have a large impact on education. (It is interesting to note that random access is one application with which the videotape recorder cannot compete.)

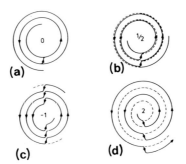

FIG. 38.   Illustration of light beam control for (a) freeze frame, (b) slow motion ($\frac{1}{2}\times$) forward, (c) reverse motion at normal speed, (d) fast motion ($2\times$) forward. (From Compaan and Kramer, 1974.)

FIG. 39. Two-sided recording on transparent disc. (From Hrbek, 1974. Copyright © 1974 by the Society of Motion Picture and Television Engineers, Inc., Scarsdale, New York. Reprinted with permission.)

In addition to "freeze frame," the inertia-less steering of the laser beam makes other features possible. Fig. 38b shows slow ($\frac{1}{2} \times$) motion forward through repeating the jump-back pulse every second revolution; Figs. 38c and 38d illustrate reverse motion at normal speed and forward motion at accelerated ($2 \times$) speed.

I would like to conclude this review article on a personal note. A mere summing up of technologies tends to leave the impression of a well-organized enterprise, inexorably leading to an optimum solution. It does not convey any of the excitement inherent in anticipating inventions, nor the disappointment experienced when they do not work. More important perhaps, a review indicates maturity of development, a certain hardening of technological positions. In the case of video discs, with at least four companies (RCA, Thomson–CSF, Philips, and Telefunken), that have invested a great deal of money (Adler 1976b), it would be unrealistic to deny this. Yet, because of economic pressure, many possibilities have not been fully explored; I already pointed out, in Section III, the opportunities afforded by the redundancy in the television signal. There are more examples, but let me discuss just one to illustrate graphically what is meant. This example has to do with playing time. In the recommended standards the playing time is $\frac{1}{2}$ hr, dictated basically by the minimum trackspacing allowed for tolerable crosstalk. The definition of "tolerable" is in turn based on each track carrying a completely separate picture, such as would be the case for the educational applications mentioned earlier. For regular programs much more crosstalk can be tolerated, and at Zenith we have, in fact, recorded such material at a density of 900 lines/mm without ill effects on image quality. Moreover, we have also recorded on both sides of a transparent disc (although only at 450 tracks/mm) and managed to select the desired side by proper focusing. This is shown in Fig. 39 (Hrbek, 1974). Thus certain avenues still remain for exploration; it is my hope, as one interested in technology, that these avenues will, in fact, be further explored.

References

Abramson, A. (1955). A short history of television recording, *JSMPTE* **64,** 72.

Abramson, A. (1973). A short history of television recording—II, *JSMPTE* **32,** 188.

Adler, R., (1974). An optical video disc player for N.T.S.C. receivers, *IEEE Trans. Broadcast Telev. Receivers* **20,** 230.

Adler, R., (1976a). "Elasto-Optic Device for Spot Wobble in a Video Disc Player," U.S. Patent 3, 985, 952.

Adler, R., (1976b). Video disc system alternatives, *IEEE Trans. Consum. Electron.* **CE 22,** 302.

Ahmed, M., Brown, R., and Korpel, A. (1975). The aerodynamic stabilization of video discs, *IEEE Trans. Consumer Electron.* **CE 21** (2), 131–139.

Barstow, G. M. (1955). The ABCs of color television, *Proc. IRE* **43,** 1574.

Bartolini, R. A. (1974). Characteristics of relief phase holograms recorded in photoresist, *Appl. Opt.* **13** (1), 169.

Beesley, M. J., and Castledine, J. G. (1970). The use of photoresist as a holographic recording medium, *Appl. Opt.* **9** (12), 2720.

Boegels, P. W. (1976). System coding parameters, mechanics and electromechanics of the reflective video disc player, *IEEE Trans. Consum. Electron.* **CE 22,** 309.

Bouwhuis, G., and Burgstede, P. (1973). The optical scanning system of the Philips "VLP" record player, *Philips Tech. Rev.,* **33** (7), 186. Also in *JSMPTE* **83** (7) , 572 (1974).

Bricot, C., Lehureau, J. C., and Puech, C. (1976). Optical readout of video disc, *IEEE Trans. Consum. Electron.* **CE 22,** 304.

Broadbent, K. D. (1974). A review of the MCA disco-vision system, *JSMPTE* **83** (7), 553.

Broussaud, G., Spitz, E., Tinet, C. M., and le Carvennec, F. L. (1974).

A video disc optical design, *1974 S.I.D. Int. Symp. Dig. Tech. Pap.*, p. 38. Lewis Winner, New York.

Clemens, J. K. (1976). Videodisc systems with contacting pickups, *1976 S.I.D. Int. Symp. Dig. Tech. Pap.*, p. 162. Lewis Winner, New York.

Compaan, K., and Kramer, P. (1973). The Philips "VLP" system, *Philips Tech. Rev.* **33** (7), 178. Also in *JSMPTE,* **83** (7), 564.

Compaan, K., and Kramer, P. (1974). An optical readout video disc system with optoelectronic tracking, *1974 S.I.D. Int. Symp. Dig. Tech. Pap.*, p. 40. Lewis Winner, New York.

Dickopp, G., and Redlich, H. (1973). Design simplicity cut costs for German color-video disk system, *Electronics* **46,** 93.

Dinsdale, A. (1927). Television sees in darkness and records its impressions, *Radio News*, June 1927, p. 1422.

Fink, D. G. (1952). "Television Engineering." McGraw–Hill, New York.

Fink, D. G. (1957). "Television Engineering Handbook." McGraw–Hill, New York.

Fink, D. G., *et al.* (1975). "Electronic Engineers' Handbook," Sect. 20. McGraw–Hill, New York.

Goldmark, P. C. (1970). Color electronic video recording, *JSMPTE* **79,** 677.

Hannan, W. J., *et al.* (1973). Holo tape: A low-cost prerecorded television system using holographic storage, *JSMPTE,* **82** (11), 905.

Hrbek, G. W. (1974). An experimental optical videodisc playback system, *JSMPTE* **83** (7), 580.

Janssen, P. J. M., and Day, P. E. (1973). Control mechanisms in the Philips "VLP" record player, *Philips Tech. Rev.* **33** (7), 190. Also in *JSMPTE* **83,** (7), 576 (1974).

Jerome, J. A., and Kaczorowski, E. M. (1974a). Film based videodisc system, *JSMPTE* **83** (7), 560.

Jerome, J. A., and Kaczorowski, E. M. (1974b). Home video-disk system creates a new image on photographic film, *Electronics* **47,** 114.

Kaczorowski, E. M., and Jerome, J. A. (1974). A photooptical video disc system, *1974 S.I.D. Int. Symp. Dig. Tech. Pap.*, p. 36. Lewis Winner, New York.

Kenney, G. C. (1976). Special purpose applications of the optical videodisc system, *IEEE Trans. Consum. Electron.* **CE 22,** 327.

Korpel, A. (1974a). Optical video disc technology, *Proc. SPIE* **53,** Laser Recording, San Diego, California.

Korpel, A. (1974b). A review of video disc principles, *1974 S.I.D. Int. Symp. Dig. Tech. Pap.*, p. 32. Lewis Winner, New York.

Korpel, A. (1976). "Video Disc." U.S. Patent 3, 931, 459.

Korpel, A. (1977). A review of video disc technology, *Avtometria* **5,** 62 (in Russian).

Kressel, H., Olsen, G. H., and Nuese, C. J. (1977). Visible $GaAs_{0.7}P_{0.3}$ cw heterojunction lasers, *Appl. Phys. Lett.* **30** (5), 249.

Lathi, B. P. (1968). "Communication Systems." Wiley, New York.

Laub, L. J. (1976). Optics of reflective video disc players, *IEEE Trans. Consum. Electron.,* **CE 22,** 258.

McIlwain, K. and Dean, C. E. (1956). "Principles of Color Television." Wiley, New York.

Mathieu, M. (1977). A random access system adapted for the optical video disc: Its impact on information retrieval, *JSMPTE,* **86** (2), 80.

Michael, M. S., and McFee, R. (1973). "Recording sound photographically on paper disks," *J. Audio Eng. Soc.* **21** (3), 187–190.

Morikawa, T., Mitsusashi, Y., and Shimada, J. (1976). Return beam induced oscillations in self-coupled semiconductor laser, *Electron. Lett.* **12** (17), 435.

Palermo, P., Korpel, A., Dickinson, G., and Watson, W. (1977). Video disc mastering and replication, *Laser Technol.* **10,** 169–174.

New Products (1970). *JSMPTE* **79,** 880.

Rice, P., Macovski, A., Jones, E. D., Frohback, H., Crews, R. W., and Noon, A. W. (1970). An experimental television recording and playback system using photographic discs, *JSMPTE* **79,** 997.

Stone, R. F. (1976). A practical narrow-band television system: Sample dot, *IEEE Trans. Broadcasting* **BC-22** (2), 21–32.

Takeda, Y., and Tsunoda, Y. (1977). The use of heterostructure diode lasers in video disc systems, *1977 IEEE/OSA Conf. Laser Eng. App. Digest Tech. Pap.*, p. 14.

Tsunoda, Y., and Takeda, Y. (1974). High density image-storage holograms by a random phase sampling method, *Appl. Opt.* **13** (9), 2046.

Tsunoda, Y., *et al.* (1976). Holographic video disk: an alternative approach to optical video disks, *Appl. Opt.* **15** (6), 1398.

Tsunoda, Y., *et al.* (1977). Semiconductor laser pickup for optical video disc player, *IEEE Trans. Consum. Elect., Proc. 1977 Spring Conf.*

vanden Bussche, W., Hoogendyk, A. H., and Wessels, J. H. (1973).

Signal processing in the Philips "VLP" system, *Philips Tech. Rev.* **33** (7), 181. Also in *JSMPTE,* **33,** (7), 567.

Whitman, R. L. (1974). A transmission mode optical video disc system, *1974 S.I.D. Int. Symp. Dig. Tech. Pap.*, p. 34. Lewis Winner, New York.

Winslow, J. (1976a). The optical videodisc, *1976 S.I.D. Int. Symp. Dig. Tech Pap.*, pp. 164–165. Lewis Winner, New York.

Winslow, J. S. (1976b). Mastering and replication of reflective videodiscs, *IEEE Trans. Consum. Electron.* **CE 22,** 318.

Wossidlo, K. H. (1976). "Tracking Arrangement." U.S. Patent 3,-946,166.

HIGH-SPEED LASER PRINTING SYSTEMS

Gary K. Starkweather

Xerox Corporation
Palo Alto Research Center
Palo Alto, California

I. Introduction

The advent of the continuous-wave laser has enabled many technologies to advance significantly, especially high-speed image recording. The very high radiance of the laser as well as the highly directional

LASER APPLICATIONS, VOLUME 4

and confined beam that it emits have permitted many technologies that had been known for years to move from the laboratory curiosity stage to the product environment. Flying-spot scanning technology has been one major benefactor of the laser and the technologies that it has enabled. This article will describe how high-speed laser scan systems are used to produce images that are both pleasing to the user and clearly are at least the equal of images that are generated not just by impact printers but by other forms of printing as well. Several systems are currently on the market such as the Xerox 9700, IBM 3800, and the Siemens ND-2. Since the electronic systems that generate the images for these printers are fascinating and have been enabled by the "electronics revolution," a final section dealing with the significant aspects of the elctronic image generation is included.

II. Scanning Systems

Flying-spot scanning systems are not new (Crews and Rice, 1961). The utility of creating images with a point of light has been apparent from the first days of facsimile. Television is, of course, the most popular single example of a nonprinting flying-spot scanning system. Most flying-spot printers have until recently utilized cathode ray tubes (CRTs) as the light source. Electron beams can be controlled and deflected with electronic signals, and the phosphor on which the electron beam impinges generates the exposing radiation. The laser has come of age along with techniques for cost-effectively modulating and deflecting light beams, such that the laser is rapidly revolutionizing printing and image generation. Since electronic signals are unidimensional (time), it is optimal if the imaging system can make direct use of such signals. Scanning with a point of light is one way in which to accomplish this task.

Shown in Fig. 1 is a simple diagram of a laser flying-spot printer. The light beam from the laser L, proceeds through a modulator M, which impresses the video data or intelligence onto the beam in the form of intensity variations. The reader should note that for the purposes of our discussions in this article the intensity information is binary (1s or 0s) as opposed to analog. For other purposes, analog-intensity modulation is of course also possible. The modulated beam then passes to the deflector D, which causes the beam to spatially scan the photosensitive media P. In most laser scan systems some form of scan

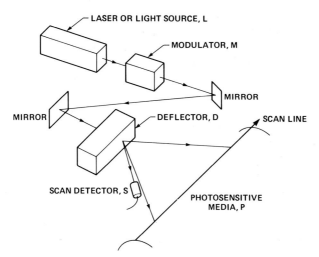

FIG. 1.   Simple flying-spot scanner.

detection is necessary in order to synchronize the scan beam with the video data. For the purposes of illustration a scan detector S is shown in the figure. Although this figure is simplistic, we shall see later on just how such systems increase in complication when the practicalitites of real systems are taken into account.

Let us assume for the moment that we wish to create a document-printing system with flying-spot scan techniques. The parameters that are required for such a system can then be calculated for future comparison as to the applicability of various technological options. We shall take as our base specifications a printer that runs at 300 spots/in. and generates two (2) 8.5 × 11-in. pages/sec. With normal interdocument gaps, etc., this corresponds to approximately 20 in./sec linear image generation. The choice of 300 scans to the inch is not arbitrary. It is currently the highest scan density available on the market and is chosen mainly for example. Other scan densities will be referenced as other manufacturers' devices are described.

Since our scan density was chosen at 300 spots/in. (300 square), then there are 9×10^4 spots/in.^{2} or $\sim 1.4 \times 10^4$ spots/cm^2. Since an 8.5 × 11-in. document contains 93.5 in.^{2} or 603 cm^2, then each page contains 8.4×10^6 points. If the printer runs at 2 pages/sec, then the laser scan system must produce a minimum of ~ 17 million points/sec. This is a nontrivial rate not only for the scanning system but for the electronics that generate the video information. In actuality, some non-scanning time must be spent to set up electronics, provide beam "re-trace" as we shall see later, and provide for interdocument gaps in the imaging path, etc. For this hypothetical printer whose specifications are similar to the Xerox 9700, the true rate is ~20 × 10⁶ points/sec or 50 nsec/point. Thus, high-speed printing, which we shall define as greater than 1 document/sec, can put significant demands on both the imaging and electronics subsystems. We shall see in this article how significant these demands are and how some typical systems have coped with the calculated requirements.

For the rest of this article, the term *pixel* and *bit* will refer to an image element, namely a spot of light that is either turned on or off at the photosensitive surface. For our discussion of printers, the image shall be composed of binary digits or "bits." Thus, in the previous example, the data rate is 20 Mbits/sec. The printers and scanners that will be considered print images that consist of either "0s" or "1s" as mentioned earlier. Any attempt to achieve gray scale via digital half-tone schemes are referenced (Roetling, 1977a, b; Bayer, 1973) at the end of the article but are not considered here. For a scanning system in general, it can be simply shown that that system bandwidth B in Mbits/sec is

$$B = V_{d}(R_{s})^{2}W_{d}$$

where V_{d} is the velocity of the photosensitive medium, W_{d} is the document or scan width, and R_{s} is the system scan density and assumes that the scan density in both directions is the same. For a system having dissimilar resolutions along the X (fast scan) and Y (slow scan) directions, R_{s} is merely the product of the X resolution, R_{x}, and Y-resolution, R_{y}. As we shall see later on, this is not always the case. For the example given, however, $V_{d} = 20$ in./sec, $W_{d} = 11$ in., and $R_{s} = 300$ bits/in. or scans/in. This yields $B = 19.8$ Mbits/sec for the *minimum* required system bandwidth.

Figure 2 is a graph of the system bandwidth B as a function of the resolution R_{s}. The curves are labeled for the document width W_{d} and the photosensitive media velocity V_{d}. The systems that are described in this article all use the xerographic process for rendering the laser-created latent image into marks on paper. This process is described elsewhere (Moore, 1972; Claus, 1969) and will be referenced in other

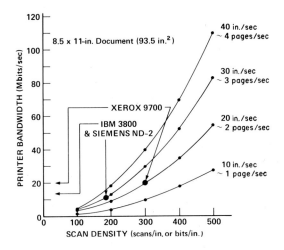

FIG. 2.   Graph of system bandwidth vs. resolution.

places in this article as the need requires. Typical xerographic photoreceptors (Chen, 1978) require anywhere from 5 to 39 ergs/cm^2 for adequate exposure. If we consider a median discharge energy of 15 ergs/cm^2 as typical, then writing an 11-in. width at 20 in./sec would require

$$11 \times 20 \times (2.54)^2 \times 15$$

or 21,290 ergs/sec or ~2 mW.

Thus, the exposure of the photoreceptor alone would require a 2-mW laser beam power. Since scan systems are not necessarily efficient and may have throughput efficiencies of only 10 – 15%, lasers having an output power in excess of 15–20 mW are required. This is not an unreasonable power level, of course, but is not particularly comfortable either. We shall discuss the laser question further on.

The laser scan systems we shall consider are comprised of the light source, via the laser, the modulator for gating the beam, the deflection apparatus for scanning the modulated beam, the imaging optics, and some type of scan detection or triggering electronics for synchronization of the beam with the data source. Subsequent descriptions of each of these subsystems or modules follows with some consideration given to the practical limits of such components.

III. Lasers

The choice of laser in the scanning system is directly dependent on the photoreceptor that is utilized in the xerographic marking subsystem. The marking subsystem does not have to be necessarily xerographic of course, but in the systems discussed in this article, xerography is used exclusively. One can easily prove the incompatibility of cathode ray tubes (CRTs) as exposure sources with xerographic systems operating in raster scan mode and at high page rates. CRTs have been used, however, in moderate speed systems. The laser provides a stable and easily manipulated light source for raster scan applications. This section on lasers is purposely short since the implications of high-speed and high-resolution scanning have little if any impact on the laser itself except for power requirements. This, as we shall see, is not so with regard to other system components. A good overview of gas lasers for data-recording purposes can be found in Buzzard (1976).

A. HELIUM–NEON LASERS

There are currently only three laser types that are applicable to reliable high-speed systems. The first and most well understood is of course the familiar helium–neon laser. The He–Ne laser is the least complicated gas laser available. As shown in Fig. 3, this laser type emits at 632.8 nm; it can be procured in powers from approximately 1 mW up to 50 mWatts. The He–Ne laser has quick warm-up characteristics in the lower power configurations (15 mW and less) and is a relatively well-behaved light source. Red photosensitive materials tend to be rarer, however, than blue and blue–green or "orthochromatic" materials. This renders the He–Ne laser somewhat less useful relative to its two technological companions discussed next. He–Ne lasers do not have a particularly high power per unit length capability. Most production units are loaded at ~0.1–0.2 mW/cm in typical units but do vary to some extent. This means that a 20-mW unit would be about a meter long. This is not prohibitive but does require careful mounting and internal support of the resonator for powers in excess of ~15 mW. Furthermore, a longer warm-up period is required for these large powers to enable the support structure to come to thermal equilibrium. It is sufficient to say that the He–Ne laser is the best choice for systems requiring powers of less than ~20 – 25 mW, pro-

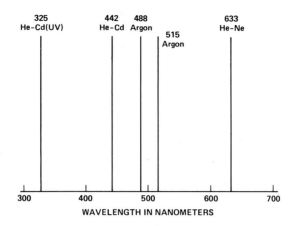

FIG. 3.   Graph of major laser wavelengths.

viding of course that sufficient sensitivity exists at 633 nm. He–Ne lasers, especially in the smaller power configurations, have exhibited lifetimes from 5000 hr to more than 20,000 hr in some cases. Several manufacturers provide warranties for more than a year and a half on the smaller units. Even though the best of the lasers we shall discuss, He–Ne lasers do not have a high light generation efficiency (light watts out/electrical watts in). Typical units run ~0.03%. Thus a 10-mW He–Ne laser might require ~300 W electrical power. While inefficient in a sense, this power requirement is actually small compared to the power consumed in the xerographic fusing station (e.g., ~2000 W).

He–Ne lasers have been the most popular and are currently the most cost-effective units available. The reader is referred to any good laser text for review of this technology.

B. Argon-Ion Lasers

Moving toward the blue end of the spectrum, the next laser of interest is the argon-ion laser. In the visible portion of the spectrum this laser has two principal emission lines. These emission lines are at 488 and 515 nm. The argon laser has the best gain per unit length of the three laser types we shall discuss. Offsetting this advantage, however, is its poor electrical efficiency. Argon lasers are available from approximately 15 mW to several watts. The larger lasers are water cooled and hence do not lend themselves readily to printers unless self-contained cooling units are tolerated. The smaller air-cooled argon units can be operated as high as 20–25 mW. The argon laser is not very efficient, converting only about 0.003% of the input electrical power to light. Fortunately, a little goes a long way and even with this low efficiency the laser would represent a small portion of the power budget. Two particular advantages of the argon laser are a fast warm-up and a fairly "quiet" beam, i.e., not much intensity fluctuation with time. Tube life is somewhat dependent on utilization profile but can be in excess of several thousand hours, which is quite acceptable. The unit loading (power per unit length) of the argon laser is also high and therefore this type of laser would only be ~$\frac{1}{3}$ as long as a He–Ne laser of equivalent power.

To the author's knowledge, there are no argon lasers in commercial printers such as those discussed in this article. While there may currently be no low-power units in commercial equipment, there are certainly many commercial pieces of equipment that contain high-power argon lasers. Perhaps in time, the virtues of argon laser technology will become more useful to those system designs unable to use He–Ne lasers. An extensive review of argon-ion laser technology can be found in Dunn and Ross (1976).

C. Helium–Cadmium Lasers

The last laser that we shall briefly discuss is the helium–cadmium type. This laser heats cadmium metal to the vaporization point to fill the discharge tube with cadmium vapor. It has reasonable unit loading (~2× He–Ne) and has the chief advantage of emitting light at 442 nm. This renders many photosensitive materials usable that were excluded from consideration with just He–Ne or in some cases argon. He–Cd lasers are not particularly efficient, being about midway between He–Ne and argon. He–Cd lasers can be obtained in powers ranging from a few milliwatts to ~50 mW. A systems disadvantage is a several-minute warm-up that is required with this laser type. This is needed since the cadmium vapor that is used for laser operation must be obtained by vaporizing cadmium metal. Unlike the two laser types above, if a He–Cd laser is turned off for any reason one must wait 10–15 min before attempting to restrike the discharge. He–Cd lasers have been variously manufactured by perhaps four or five companies over the past few years. Currently, however, only Liconix, Inc., in Santa Clara, California and Spectra-Physics in Mountain View, California make commercial units for outright sale. RCA, who made the Model 2186 He–Cd laser, no longer sells these units.

The lifetime of He–Cd lasers is somewhat uncertain, but some innovations are lengthening the probable lifetimes to ~2000–4000 hr. The He–Cd laser is a usable laser type for high-speed printers. A Xerox proprietary version of He–Cd technology is used in the Xerox 9700 computer printer. One should in all fairness observe that He–Cd laser technology is considerably younger than either He–Ne or argon. Some of its disadvantages, therefore, may be overcome with an equivalent amount of technology investment.

D. SOLID STATE LASERS

Any current discussion of laser technology would not be complete without mention of solid state lasers. These diode lasing units are quite efficient and compact. Solid state room-temperature units are available from Hitachi, Exxon, and others. A major advantage of the solid state laser, is of course, the fact that it is directly modulatable. No auxiliary modulation scheme is necessary, thus impacting system cost and reliability positively. The lifetimes of solid state lasers should have no trouble exceeding gas laser equivalent units as the technology matures. The exit beam of solid state lasers does require some special optical treatment for proper optical system utilization, but this is not a significant disadvantage.

The primary disadvantage of solid state lasers to date has been the near-infrared output they provide. Most units emit in the 800–900 nm region and this is a poor match with most available photoconductors. It should be noted that while this is a significant disadvantage, Canon, Inc., has recently announced the availability of a laser printer, designated the LBP-10, which uses a solid state laser diode as the exposure source. Typical solid state lasers have moderate output powers that range from ~5 to 35 mW or sometimes greater. The more cost-effective units are also the lower power units currently. While current infrared laser diodes do not provide adequate performance matching to available xerographic photosensitive media, they promise to be a powerful future laser source.

IV. Modulators

There are essentially two types of modulator worth considering for the purposes of our discussions in this article. These types are the electrooptic modulator based on the Pockels (1893) effect and acoustooptic modulation derived from the Debye–Sears (1932) effect. The actual systems described in this article utilize the latter phenomena and hence we shall spend the greater part of our modulator discussions on the acoustooptic modulator technology. This discussion is not intended to be exhaustive with regard to modulator physics. Sufficient detail, however, is given to understand the limitations of the two modulator types discussed earlier with respect to their use in high-speed printing systems. Should the reader be interested in an extensive bibliography on optical modulation, Ellis and Walton (1971) is suggested. This article provides extensive references on acoustooptic, electrooptic, magnetooptic, mechanical, and other modulation techniques.

A. ELECTROOPTIC MODULATORS

The Pockels cell is based on an electrooptic effect similar to the Kerr effect (Born and Wolf, 1966). As shown in Fig. 4, the field is applied transversely to the light beam and the resultant electrooptic effect is dependent on the square of the applied field E. The Pockels cell applies the field longitudinally to the light beam as shown in Fig. 5 and uses a crystal instead of a liquid as in the Kerr cell. Since the Pockels effect depends on the field E rather than its square, the voltage required to operate a Pockels cell is considerably less than a Kerr cell. Even so, Pockels-effect devices for laser modulation often require from 100 to 300 V to operate and as we shall see, this does complicate the driving circuitry.

In Fig. 6, a typical Pockels-cell modulator setup is shown. A polarizer is placed in the laser or light beam and linearly polarizes the light. The polarizer must be oriented so that the plane of polarization is oriented parallel to either the X or Y crystallographic axes of the electrooptic material. The cell electrodes are on the faces of the crystal so that the light to be modulated must pass through the electrode. Applying voltage to the electrodes as shown causes the crystal to induce a retardation because of a refractive index change. An analyzer placed after the modulator causes the light exiting it to vary in intensity as the voltage on the cell is varied. With no voltage, the analyzer is

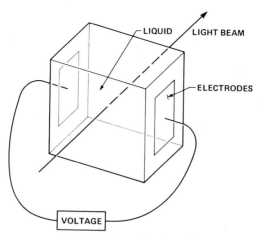

FIG. 4.   Kerr-cell schematic.

adjusted to produce no transmitted light. If sufficient voltage is applied to cause a half-wave retardation, then maximum light transmission through the system is realized. This is called the half-wave voltage, $V_{\lambda/2}$. With this voltage applied, the components of the light beam that are orthogonal to each other have undergone a relative phase shift of 180°. The plane of polarization therefore undergoes a 90° rotation. The analyzer at the cell beam exit resolves this phase or polarization change

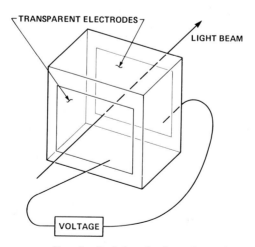

FIG. 5.   Pockels-cell schematic.

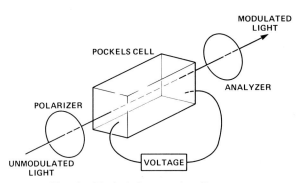

FIG. 6. Typical electrooptic-cell setup.

into intensity variations. The polarizer and analyzer can be constructed from Glan–Thompson or Wollaston prisms, for example. There are several possibilities for electrode configurations as described in the literature (Goldstein, 1968). The use of low-power lasers allows the electrodes to reside on the entrance and exit windows of the crystal. The only disadvantage of this type of configuration is some transmission loss. The absorption of the electrode causes sufficient heating in high-power applications to require electrode modification as described in Goldstein (1968).

It can be shown that the intensity out I_{out} is related to the intensity in I_{in} by the following relation

$$\frac{I_{out}}{I_{in}} = \sin^2 \pi \left(\frac{\eta_0^3 r_{63} V_z}{\lambda} \right) \tag{1}$$

where η_0 is the ordinary index of refraction of the crystal, r_{63} is the electrooptic constant in micrometers per volt $\times 10^{-6}$, V_z is the longitudinally applied voltage in volts, and λ is the wavelength of light in microns. The quantity in parenthesis then becomes the number of wavelengths retarded, N. For full modulation, $N = \frac{1}{2}$ wave.

Two typical crystals that are used in electrooptic modulators are potassium dihydrogen phosphate, KDP, and potassium dideuterium phosphate, KD*P. Although there are other candidates for electrooptic materials, KDP and KD*P are the most widely used in general, and KD*P permits the lowest operating voltages. In an actual modulator, several crystals are "stacked" together longitudinally to decrease the voltage requirement. Table I lists the important parameters such as η_0 and r_{63} for KDP, KD*P, and an older material ammonium dihydrogen

TABLE I

ELECTROOPTICAL MATERIALS

Material	r_{63} (μm/V $\times$ 10^{-6})	$V_{1/2}$ (kV) (λ ~550 nm)	~η_0
ADP			
ammonium dihydrogen phosphate	8.5	9.2	1.526
KDP			
potassium dihydrogen phosphate	10.5	7.5	1.51
KD*P[a]			
potassium dideuterium phosphate	26.4	2.9[a]	1.52

[a] ~99% deuterium.

phosphate. Also listed is the relative voltage required for half-wave retardation.

As is evident from Eq. (1), the output and input beams vary sinusoidally with the applied voltage. Thus if one should want to output a linear light level variation, some compensation of the driver and cell setup is required (Goldstein,1968). Since our concern here is two-level or on–off modulation only, then the reader is referred to Goldstein (1968) and Bracale and Lombardi (1970) for further details.

One undesirable characteristic of electrooptic modulators is the rather rapid variation of the electrooptic constant with temperature. This temperature variability requires in general a cell bias point adjustment. This adjustment can be manual or automatic, and is determined by sending alternate "1s" and "0s" and monitoring cell contrast. This temperature dependence is usually sensitive enough to require adjustment for temperature effects from the general environment and from cell heating caused by changes in the data load.

There are several papers available on electrooptic cell driving circuits, for example, White (1971). The basic driver task is driving the capacitive load of the electrooptic cell. A typical high-speed laser modulator might have a capacitance of 100–200 pF. This small capacitance might seem insignificant. However, simple calculation illustrates that at high speed such modulators place high demands on transistorized drivers, not just from the voltage requirements but the current as well. For example, a capacitive load stores a charge, Q at voltage, V by the relation,

$$Q = CV \tag{2}$$

where Q is the charge in coulombs, C the capacitance in farads, and V is the voltage in volts. Furthermore, the modulator rise time t places an upper limit on the amount of time available in which to charge up this capacitance. The "surge" or peak current therefore is shown by Eq. (3) as,

$$I_{pk} = \frac{Q}{t} \tag{3}$$

since current is charge per unit time. Thus if the required half-wave voltage $V_{\lambda/2}$ is 150 V, the capacitance is 120 pF, and the rise time is 10 nsec, the value of I_{pk} is

$$I_{pk} = (120 \times 10^{-12})(150)/(10^{-8})$$

or

$$I_{pk} = 1.8 \quad A$$

This is a fairly agressive load for the driving circuitry. Printing alternate "1s" and "0s" would require an average power of ~200 W. While commercial devices exist that operate in these regimes, the user should be aware that the higher the speed the greater the demands on the driver, and cell heating is data dependent. The cascading of crystals to achieve a low enough voltage to be operable with transistorized drivers also requires careful matching of the signals and crystal circuitry, since substantial currents are being switched. Development of alternate schemes of modulation using electrooptic techniques as briefly discussed at the end of this section could permit gigabit bandwidths with just a few watts of power. Real devices will probably fall quite short of this potential because of other problems, such as heating effects.

The bandwidth of the electrooptic modulator is not dependent on the laser beam dimensions. This is not so with the acoustooptic modulator to be discussed next. The electrooptic modulator has a very good contrast ratio as a result of the polarization nature on the phenomenon. Careful adjustment of electrooptic cells can yield on–off ratios of 1000 to 1 or better. A high-performance commercial system is produced by Coherent Associates. This system, called the 3050 E. O. Modulation System, has a system bandwidth of 50 MHz and a cell rise time of 7 nsec. Additionally, the contrast or extinction ratio is 500 : 1 at 632.8 nm. We can translate the 50-MHz bandwidth into approximately 100 Mbits/sec digital bandwidth. The author has found that a good approximation for systems of this type is that the digital bandwidth is approximately 1.5 times the rise time, t.

In summary, the electrooptic modulator is a well-understood technology, with potential architectural variations that might permit significant system advantages for high-speed applications. Although to the author's knowledge, no commercial products employing electrooptic modulators exist, reliable commercial electrooptic modulation systems having bandwidths as high as 50 MHz can be purchased (Coherent Associates, Danbury, Connecticut). Also, as shown in White (1971), devices having channel capacities of up to 250 Mbits/sec have been built.

B. Acoustooptic Modulators

The acoustooptic modulation technique has been described in a number of articles such as those by Korpel *et al.* (1966) and Hance and Parks (1965). This technique has been studied both experimentally and theoretically by many persons. The technique was first described by Debye and Sears in 1932. Raman and Nath (1935) also provided early insight into this now very beneficial and cost-effective technique of laser modulation. Watson and Hrbek described a high-efficiency laser intensity modulator in 1970. Since 1970 many acoustooptic modulators have become available from various manufacturers.

As shown in Fig. 7, in the acoustooptic modulator, a beam of ultrasound is launched through a liquid or solid medium and the acoustic pressure waves interact with a light beam traveling orthogonal to the sound. The pressure variations form in essence a diffraction grating that varies in refractive index with the local pressure and thus diffracts the light beam as it exits the modulator cell. The two principal types of modulator are the Debye–Sears and Bragg devices. Most early devices were based on the Debye–Sears effect, whereas modern acoustooptic modulators are Bragg devices. Debye–Sears devices are characterized by the fact that the light is diffracted into many orders. Bragg devices produce diffraction in only one principal order. Figure 7 illustrates a Bragg cell.

The transparent medium in which the interaction takes place can be made of many different types of materials. While water and glass are usable, most commercial devices utilize $PbMoO_4$, lead molybdate, or TeO_2, tellurium dioxide, with $PbMoO_4$ being predominant. The purpose of this discussion will be to describe the general parameters of acoustooptic cells and how these parameters limit modulator bandwidth. This limiting data can then be inserted appropriately into our high-speed printing calculations. As shown in Fig. 7 the radio-frequency signal from the driver is applied to a transducer that is bonded to the modulator medium. This tranducer converts the electrical rf signal into a mechanical pressure wave in the acoustic medium.

In Fig. 7 the amount of light diffracted is related to the amplitude of the sound wave. The angle 2θ is proportional to the frequency of the sound wave. For intensity modulation purposes, the frequency is kept constant while the amplitude is varied according to the modulation signal. The cell is operating in the Bragg condition when the relationship

$$w > \frac{\Lambda^2}{\lambda} \tag{4}$$

is realized, where w is the width of the sound column in the direction of light travel, Λ is the acoustic wavelength, and λ is the wavelength of light being diffracted. For the Debye–Sears condition to be met, the sense of the inequality in Eq. (4) has to be reversed. The reader should note that the transition from Debye–Sears to Bragg is gradual and not abrupt. The two regimes nevertheless are defined mathematically as above.

The selection of acoustooptic materials is based on several material parameters. An acoustic figure of merit M can be calculated, which is useful for comparing materials to be selected. The acoustic figure of merit M can be defined by the relation,

$$M = \frac{n^6 p^2}{\rho v^3} \tag{5}$$

where n is the refractive index, p is the photoelastic coefficient, ρ is the density, and v is the velocity of sound in the medium. An expression for the acoustic power required for maximum light diffraction has been given by Watson and Hrbek to be

$$P = 1.26 \frac{h}{w} \frac{1}{M_w} \left(\frac{\lambda}{\lambda_r}\right)^2 \tag{6}$$

where w is the width of the sound column (transducer width) as above, h is the thickness of the cell orthogonal to the light-beam direction, λ is the wavelength of the sound, and λ_r is the wavelength of the optical

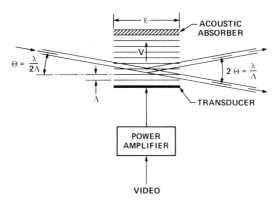

FIG. 7. Acoustooptic modulator diagram.

radiation. The parameter M_w is the ratio of the figures of merit for the medium in question and water, respectively. The figure of merit for water is ~ 160 when a He–Ne laser is used.

The reader should take special note of the previous two equations. The figure of merit favors materials having a low velocity of sound. For high-speed systems, however, the modulator rise time is very crucial. The cell rise time is essentially that time required for the acoustic wave to cross the light beam. The modulator rise time t is then described simply by the relation,

$$t = \frac{D}{v} \tag{7}$$

where v is the velocity of the sound wave and D is the diameter of the light beam in the interaction zone. This fundamental requirement means that a high velocity of sound or small beam size in the direction of acoustic wave travel or both are required for minimum rise time and hence maximum bandwidth. A very useful paper dealing with wideband modulators is that of by Boyd et al. (1977) of the Harris Corporation. It is important to observe the limitations of such cells resulting from the parametric relationships given above.

Since the wavelength of sound in the cell is the velocity of sound v divided by the frequency of the sound f, one can calculate how many compressions and rarefactions are present in the domain of the beam dimensions in the area of interaction. For example, assume a typical velocity of sound v of 4000 m/sec. Also if we assume a center frequency of 100 MHz then the acoustic wavelength is

$$\Lambda = 4000/10^8 \quad m = 40 \quad \mu m \tag{8}$$

If the laser beam diameter in the interaction zone is say 0.7 mm, as from a typical laser with no optics prior to the cell, then there would be ~17 waves in the interaction region. This is sufficient for very efficient diffraction. The rise time, however, from Eq. (7) would be approximately 175 nsec. If we consider the digital bandwidth to be $1/t$, then the effective bandwidth would be ~6 Mbits/sec. This is a rather unimpressive rate for high-speed printing. Reference to Fig. 2 illustrates that either the resolution or the throughput of the printer would be severely limited at ~6 Mbits/sec.

There are ways around the above limitation, however. One way is to increase the cell center frequency. This is not a source of significant gains, however, since the acoustic absorption of materials at frequencies greater than ~200–300 MHz becomes limiting. In fact, to the author's knowledge, no commercial devices are available with center frequencies in excess of 220 MHz. Using the velocity of sound for $PbMoO_4$, i.e., 3.63 mm/μsec, and a center frequency of 220 MHz, yields an acoustic wavelength of 16.5 μm. Also, as shown in Fig. 8, the beam can be focused cylindrically so that the beam width in the direction of the acoustic wave travel is reduced thus decreasing the rise time due to the shorter time required for the acoustic wave to cross the optical beam. If one allows two waves of interaction to be present in the beam for sufficient diffraction efficiency, then the interaction distance is 33 μm. With the sound velocity being 3.63 mm/μsec the rise time is therefore, 9.1 nsec.

This is roughly equivalent to 100 Mbits/sec and is capable of permitting impressive printing speeds and resolutions as can be seen from Fig. 2. The availability of light to expose the photoreceptor, adequate deflector scan rates, as well as the digital burden to provide intelligence at these speeds remain to be determined.

There are several articles dealing with wide-band modulator design such as those by Boyd et al. (1977), and by Johnson (1977). Polarization of the input beam can also have effects that must be considered, as shown by Lucero et al. (1976). One of the problems associated with focusing the beam in the interaction region is that the beam, instead of being collimated, has a cone or convergence angle associated with it. This angle can become large enough so that the extremities of the

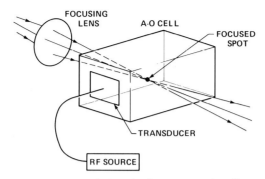

FIG. 8.   Beam focusing in acoustooptic cell.

wavefront are sufficiently off the Bragg condition to prohibit adequate diffraction efficiency from them. This means that increasing the center or carrier frequency so as to decrease the acoustic wavelength and focusing the beam smaller in the cell to decrease the rise time may not be a very good trade-off. Current state-of-the art devices have rise times of ~7 nsec. Exclusive of multichannel printing therefore, we should consider ~100 Mbits/sec an upper limit for acoustooptic modulation.

As given by Watson and Hrbek, the ratio of diffracted light I_d to incident light I_0 is given by the relation,

$$\frac{I_d}{I_0} = \sin^2\left[1.4w\left(\frac{\lambda_r}{\lambda}\right)(M_w P_s)^{1/2}\right] \tag{9}$$

where P_s is the power density in watts per square meter and the transducer length w is in meters. The other parameters were defined earlier. Looking back at the electrooptic modulator, the output beam also varies as the sine squared. Thus, for analog recording, linearization of the driver is required for linear recording. For digital recording, however, this is not a problem.

The driver for acoustooptic modulators is simple compared to electrooptic driving circuits. As shown in Fig. 9, the driver for an acoustooptic modulator consists of essentially three stages. These stages are the carrier oscillator, balanced mixer, and rf amplifier stages. The voltages required from the driver are also much more tolerable. For example, the equation

$$P = \frac{V^2}{8Z} \tag{10}$$

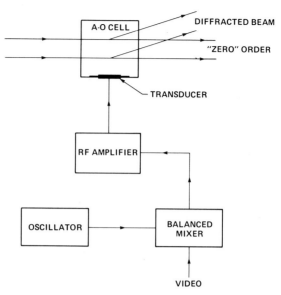

FIG. 9. Acoustooptic cell-driver diagram.

is useful, where P is the required power to diffract light, V is the peak-to-peak voltage, and Z is the cell impedance. The above relation is for sinusoidal voltage variations and is a familiar electrical engineering relationship. Typical values of P for practical cells are ~1–2 W of rf power. Cell impedance is usually designed to be 50 Ω. Thus the peak-to-peak voltage for the maximum drive power of 2 W is

$$V = (2 \times 8 \times 50)^{1/2} = 28 \quad V \tag{11}$$

This is a very attainable value with wide-band transistors. In actuality, the technology of laser printing owes some of its advances in driver technology to the citizens band radio market, which is remarkably similar in its driver requirements. The drivers are usually designed so that the input impedance is 50 Ω and the required input drive levels are compatible with transistor–transistor (TTL) logic. The acoustooptic driver is therefore a much more cost-effective device than the electrooptic driver. Also, there are virtually no temperature or data-load effects for acoustooptic devices as there are for electrooptic units and this further simplifies the ultimate printing system.

The reader should understand that it is not the purpose of this article to provide every parametric relationship for modulator design or deflector design, but to illustrate the basic limitations that the technology must face due to fundamental design parameters. An extended theoretical modeling of acoustooptic modulation is given in an article by Calligaris *et al.* (1973). The acoustooptic modulator is used in every high-speed printer employing laser technology available today. The available printers referred to are of course the Xerox 9700, the IBM 3800, and the Seimens ND-2 as mentioned at the beginning of this article. The Seimens ND-2 uses an acoustooptic *deflector* for part of its scanning operation. This aspect of acoustooptics will be discussed in the section on deflectors that follows.

A novel acoustooptic modulation scheme that permits the generation of several simultaneous beams was demonstrated by Zenith Corporation several years ago. This technique uses several acoustic frequencies applied to the transducer at once to generate multiple optical beams, and the device has come to be known as a multibeam modulator. If six frequencies are simultaneously applied to the cell, then six beams result at slightly different diffracted angles. Each beam is turned on or off by causing its frequency to be present or absent in the signal applied to the transducer. This system requires careful selection of frequencies for uniform beam separation and elimination of sum and difference problems. The light present in the "on" beams is dependent on the number of beams that are "on" since the light available for diffraction is fixed. This requires compensation circuitry that must alter the amount of power applied as a function of the number of "on" beams. As we shall see later, the Siemens 3352 printer utilizes this technique in its optical system.

There are other modulation schemes that might be useful for high-speed printing such as the interdigitated electrooptic modulator described by Polky and Harris (1972). Such devices might provide even simpler and much faster modulators in the future. For the present discussion, however, 80–100 Mbits/sec should be considered the upper limit of modulator performance in practical devices. Of course, military systems have been built that are capable of higher recording rates. The commercial environment, however, has special demands that require reliable, cost-effective operation in everyday business use.

V. Deflectors

One area of great interest in laser scanners of any kind is the deflection system. This is so since flying-spot scanning usually requires not only many spots per scan but many scans per second as well. For example, the IBM 3800 produces ~2600 spots/scan. With a process speed of ~31 in./sec (~79 cm/sec) and a resolution of 144 scans/in. in the process direction, ~4500 scans/sec are required. This means that a maximum of approximately 12×10^6 points/sec must be generated by the deflection system.

In the case of the Xerox 9700, the system produces a resolution of 300 spots/in. in both directions. With a scan width of 11 in. and a process speed of 20 in./sec (~51 cm/sec), 3300 bits/scan and 6000 scans/ sec are required, thus necessitating a deflection system capable of producing ~20×10^6 points/sec. These spot rates are not particularly phenomenal if one is familiar with the television industry. Television systems for the home are capable of generating 2–4 million spots/sec routinely and special high-performance units can generate as many as 50×10^6 points/sec.

The significance of laser deflection systems is that they deflect light beams rather than electron beams. In a cathode ray tube, for example, the electron beam strikes a phosphor that emits light and is imaged by a lens for exposing a medium. Electron beams are relatively easy to deflect. One can use magnetics, electrostatics, or some combination of the two to create either a line or an area raster scan. The problem is that CRT light sources are not very bright when compared to even a low-power laser. Thus for a high-speed printer the laser with its very high radiance has become the source of choice.

Deflection of light is difficult compared to deflection of electron beams, however. One significant advantage of light-beam scanning is that such beams are very stable against outside influences. CRT systems must be magnetically shielded, etc., to maintain beam position on the tube face. Thus the problem faced in any laser scanning system, and especially high-speed systems, is how to cost effectively scan the light beam with the required precision. The purpose of this section is to observe what deflection technology can be used and what its limits are. Also, as we shall see, practical deflectors require cooperation from the optical system as well. While there are many phenomena available to deflect light, only a few can be mentioned here and only two really deserve interest with regard to practical devices. This conclusion may be radically altered in the future as developments in integrated optics produce significant advances (Cunniff, 1973). As yet, however, nothing remotely approaching the needs of high-speed laser printing is commercially available.

Before proceeding to the available technologies for light deflection we should establish some basic equations for comparison of the deflection schemes. A basic deflector is shown in Fig. 10. In this diagram the width of the deflected beam at the deflector is W and the angle of deflection is Ψ. One can define a deflector merit function M by the relation,

$$M = W\Psi \tag{12}$$

Since the minimum angular resolution α of a uniformly illuminated circular aperture is given by the relation,

$$\alpha = \frac{1.22\lambda}{W} \tag{13}$$

we can derive the number of resolvable elements N_r that the deflector is capable of producing by combining (12) and (13) so that,

$$N_r = \frac{\Psi}{\alpha} \tag{14}$$

or

$$N_r = \frac{M}{1.22\lambda} \tag{15}$$

These equations assume that the deflecting aperture is circular and informly illuminated and that the spot is diffraction limited by the system exit pupil. For this case, the shape of the spot is described by the square of a Bessel function of first order divided by its argument. A more practical case is for a rectangular aperture, in which case the spot shape is described by the square of a sinc function $(\sin[x]/x)$. For systems having a Gaussian energy distribution the constant, 1.22 merely becomes 1.0 for all practical purposes. We can therefore utilize Eq. (12) and (15) to assess which deflector technologies are worth considering based on resolution considerations. The final decision on technology utility can then be made based upon the number of spots per second the system requires..

A. ELECTROOPTIC DEFLECTORS

Electrooptic techniques have been considered for laser deflection by several workers. The digital electrooptic deflector uses the electrooptic effect to cause a change in the refractive index of the deflector

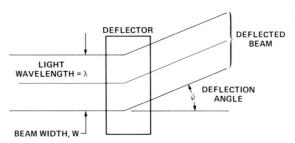

FIG. 10.   Basic deflector diagram.

material and hence steer the optical beam to one of two spots depending on whether a one or a zero is applied. Thus for n E–O cells, 2^n spots can be generated. While fast access time can be obtained, the driving circuitry can be complex for reasons cited in the section on modulators. The electrooptic device does possess the characteristic of providing random access to any position. This is not as generally true or convenient for other deflection technologies. This characteristic is not of any great utility in a high-speed laser printer, however. Furthermore, if we wish to have ~4000 spots across the scan, then a cascaded system of 12 cells would be required. The cascaded losses might be prohibitive from an efficiency standpoint. Electrooptic deflection technology can also be implemented in analog form for continuous or nondigital deflection. In general, however, these devices are quite complicated.

The electrooptic effect may be very useful in the future but as yet the required performance parameters have not been realized. A good synopsis of electrooptic deflectors and deflectors in general can be obtained in an article by Zook (1974). This article may be very useful to a reader generally unfamiliar with deflector types. In summary, the electrooptical deflector is a true "solid state" device with no moving parts, as contrasted with a polygon or galvanometer, which is clearly mechanical in nature. To date, its elegance has been more than offset by its operational complexity and inability to meet the cost/performance goals required for practical systems.

B. ACOUSTOOPTIC DEFLECTORS

We saw in the section on acoustooptic modulators how the interaction of an ultrasonic or acoustic wave with a light beam can produce modulation. This same basic phenomenon can be used to deflect light as well (Korpel *et al.*, 1966). In the acoustooptic deflector, instead of turning a carrier wave on and off to achieve modulation, the carrier wave is modulated in frequency. Thus in a modulator the light beam is diffracted at an angle that depends on frequency, but since only one frequency is present in the cell, only one deflected or diffracted position is realized. In the acoustooptic deflector multiple spatial positions of the diffracted beam are realized by multiple carrier frequencies in the cell. The frequency is usually varied as a ramp or "chirp," but can be randomly varied as desired. In fact, several frequencies can be applied simultaneously to create multiple spots. This, of course, causes the intensity of each spot to vary depending on how many spots are being generated. Special circuitry is required to balance the intensity in such a system.

A typical acoustooptic deflector setup is shown in Fig. 11. Here a signal applied to the transducer is not varied in intensity as in a modulator, but has its frequency altered to cause motion of the diffracted beam over some angle β. We shall see the dependence of angle on frequency subsequently. Lenses and other optical systems can be used to produce a beam of the proper scan width. With frequency modulation scanning (FM), i.e., a ramp of frequencies applied to the transducer, certain nonlinearities can occur. These nonlinearities can result in focusing errors as a result of the applied ramp. These nonlinearities may not always be serious, but should be considered in any application. Dickson (1972) provides good detail on these effects.

Let us now look at some of the specifics of the acoustooptic deflector

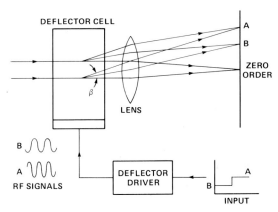

FIG. 11.   Acoustooptic deflector.

and its limitations. While this technology is not commercially used in any primary scan (full document width) applications, a variation of this technology is used in the Siemens ND-2 printer. This application will be discussed later.

First, we shall confine our interest to the Bragg effect. While this discussion will treat the acoustooptic deflector with regard to its operational limits, a significant and detailed discussion of wide-band acoustooptic deflectors is found in Alphonse (1972). With regard to merit function M, the acoustooptical deflector does not fare very well. There is always a trade-off between aperture width, which must be large to get high angular resolution, and the transit time of the acoustic wave, which must be small to allow rapid scans. A typical cell might have an aperture of 30 mm. The angle of deflection from an acoustooptic cell obeys the relation

$$\sin \Psi = \frac{\lambda}{\Lambda} \qquad \text{or} \qquad \Psi \sim \frac{\lambda}{\Lambda} \tag{16}$$

where λ is the wavelength of the optical radiation and Λ is the acoustic wavelength. This equation can also be rewritten as

$$\Psi = \frac{\lambda f}{v} \tag{17}$$

where f is the acoustic frequency and v is the acoustic velocity in the deflection medium. Equation (17) clearly illustrates that a low acoustic velocity increases the deflection angle and hence improves the deflector. By way of contrast, in a modulator where speed is essential, the velocity should be maximized. To achieve maximum deflection angle, the acoustic frequency should be maximized as well. In actuality the frequency difference (bandwidth) is what determines the maximum angular extent of deflection for a given acoustic velocity.

We may now look at some typical materials and determine what kinds of performance levels are attainable. For example, an excellent deflector material is tellurium dioxide, TeO_2. The acoustic velocity v for TeO_2 is ~4200 m/sec. Using a wavelength of 633 nm and a signal bandwidth of 100 MHz, the deflection angle Ψ is

$$\Psi = (0.633 \times 10^{-3} \times 10^8)/(4.2 \times 10^6)$$

or

$$\Psi = 15.1 \quad \text{mrad}$$

For our assumed 30-mm aperture, the minimum resolvable angle α would be,

$$\alpha \sim (0.633 \times 10^{-3})/30$$

or

$$\alpha = 2.11 \times 10^{-5} \quad \text{rad}$$

Thus the number of resolvable elements turns out to be ~700. This is not very exciting for a full document scan. We should like at least 2500 spots to be interesting at all.

If we choose $PbMoO_4$ which has an acoustic velocity of 3630 m/sec, an acoustic bandwidth of 150 MHz (a high number), and let the aperture grow to 50 mm then the number of resolvable spots becomes

$$N_r = (1.5 \times 108) \times (50)/(3.63 \times 106)$$

or

$$N_r = 2066 \quad \text{spots}$$

Even with this aggressive use of the technology we fall short of our goal. For this reason no acoustooptic deflectors are used exclusively for scan-line generation. If the carrier center frequency is 200 MHz, then a 150-MHz bandwidth requires the cell to process signals ranging from say 125 to 275 MHz. This requires optimizing the transducer for beam steering and efficient diffraction. Coquin et al. (1970) have described a deflector with a 300-MHz center frequency, a bandwidth of 280 MHz, and a 10-element stepped transducer array.

It can also be shown that the number of resolvable elements in an acoustooptic deflector is given by the relation,

$$N = \tau \, \Delta f \tag{18}$$

where τ is the acoustic transit time and Δf is the bandwidth of the cell. The acoustic transit time τ is,

$$\tau = \frac{W}{v} \tag{19}$$

where W is the cell aperture and v the velocity of sound.

We can therefore calculate the number of resolvable elements for our TeO_2 cell above. The following calculation substitutes W/v for τ:

$$N = (30)(100 \times 10^6)/(4.2 \times 10^6)$$

or

$$N = 714 \quad \text{spots}$$

Thus the resolution is the same as that predicted by the optical formulation in Eq. (14). The acoustooptic deflector is thus faced with a
severe problem if it is to achieve high resolution. The bandwidth must
be high and the transit time must also be high. Acoustic velocities in
practical solids vary little. The acoustic attenuation in cells poses a
limit to cell size. The ability to steer the acoustic beam to provide good
diffraction efficiency across the scan, and attenuation of the acoustic
wave in the cell, limit cell size and bandwidth, thus limiting resolution.
It seems unlikely at this point in time that cells producing more than
2000 spots are possible in practical systems. We shall see later that the
Siemens ND-2 printer uses an acoustooptic deflector in a novel way
but not for primary scan generation. From our previous data it can be
seen that the deflector merit function M for TeO_2,

$$M = (30)(15.1 \times 10^{-3}) = 0.45 \quad mm$$

This value should be remembered for later comparison with other
deflection technologies or schemes. The $PbMoO_4$ system with 50-mm
aperture and 150-MHz bandwidth would have a merit function M of

$$M = (50)(26.2 \times 10^{-3}) = 1.31 \quad mm$$

and this appears to be a practical upper bound. The author is not aware
of any literature describing devices with a resolution N_r or a merit
function M that are better than our hypothetical device. Design details
have been purposely avoided here, since the literature abounds with
this information and this article is intended to be a systems discussion
as opposed to device design.

One method to get around the cell resolution problem is by the addition of a traveling-wave acoustooptic deflector (Foster et al., 1970).
As shown in Fig. 12 the traveling-wave cell causes additional focusing
of the deflected beam so as to reduce the effective minimum resolvable
angle α. This of course increases the number of resolvable elements
by Eq. (14). The traveling-lens technique can use an acoustooptic cell
or mechanical ribbon, etc., as described in Foster et al. (1970). While
this technique can potentially increase the resolution of an acoustooptic
cell by at least an order of magnitude, no practical devices have yet
emerged on the market. Such an approach has several drawbacks that
should be mentioned. First, the cell transit time is relatively fixed, thus
fixing the scan rate. Additionally, significant acoustic power must be
applied to a cell several inches in length and this may require cooling
or special thermal stabilization. The traveling-wave lens is nevertheless

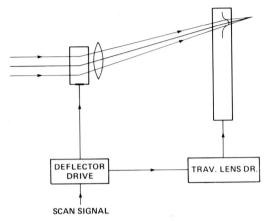

FIG. 12. Traveling acoustooptic lens.

a novel and innovative technique to enhance the utility of an acoustooptic cell for high-resolution purposes.

VI. Galvanometers

The galvanometer is probably the earliest of light deflectors. It consists basically of a mirror fastened to an armature that is supported in a field produced by either permanent magnets or electromagnets. The actual support of the galvanometer is either by a fiber such as quartz, a band of metal, or physical bearings that support a rotatable shaft. In general the galvanometer can be made to follow an input electrical signal, and hence a sawtooth or ramp signal can be applied for scanning. Honeywell, General Scanning, and MFE Industries are major producers of galvanometers. Since the galvanometer is a mechanical oscillator, it has a bandwidth that must be understood so that its limits can be ascertained. P. J. Brosens (1971) has described driving techniques that permit the galvanometer to scan in a sawtooth fashion.

The galvanometer can easily have scan angles in excess of 20° and mirror sizes of a centimeter. This means that, from Eqs. (14) and (15), the resolution N_r is,

$$N_r = (2)(20)(\pi/180)(10 \text{ mm})/(0.633 \times 10^{-3})$$

or

$$N_r \sim 11,000 \quad \text{spots}$$

The factor 2 comes from the doubling of the angle of the deflected light due to reflection, and He–Ne laser light is assumed. The merit function M for the galvanometer is therefore,

$$M = W\Psi$$

or

$$M = 7.0 \quad mm$$

This is considerably higher than the best acoustooptical deflector with respect to the spots-per-scan potential. The galvanometer has one glaring deficiency that eliminates it from contention as a high-speed deflector for laser systems, and that is its slow scanning rate. Any deflector that would be of use to us must be able to produce at least 4000 scans/sec. The 9700 scanner produces 6000 scans/sec, for example. Galvanometers can be made that scan at these rates sinusoidally but this is in general not very desirable and such galvanometers can usually only deflect 2°–3° at these rates. The reflective mirror must also be quite small. Typically only 1–3 mm is permitted. Thus the merit function for such a device would become

$$M = (2)(0.105)$$

$$= 0.21 \quad mm$$

which is poorer than that of the acoustooptical deflector.

The galvanometer fails to meet out criterion of ~3000 spots/scan *and* 4000 scans/sec. The acoustooptical deflector also failed this requirement. We shall therefore continue on to a discussion of the final form of deflector, the polygon, which fortunately meets and exceeds our requirements. The galvanometer has found practical use in laser devices such as the Xerox Telecopier 200 facsimile transceiver, the Harris Associated Press facsimile system, and in point-of-sale terminal (POS) technology. These devices are, however, far less demanding on a spots per second basis than are high-speed printers.

VII. Polygonal Scanners

The polygonal scanner represents a fascinating deflector technology. At least from outward appearances it is the most primitive of the deflection technologies available for high-speed scanning. Polarization effects, the interaction of light with sound, etc., are clearly more "modern" and advanced than a multifaceted mirror on the end of a motor. The fact is, however, that even for medium speed applications and especially for high-speed printer applications, this technology out-classes all competitors to date. We shall soon see why this is so.

As shown in Fig. 13, the polygonal scanner is composed of a mul-tifaceted mirror, which is usually in the form of a "disk" configuration, a driving motor that can be electrical or air driven, and a control system to power the motor and control its speed as necessary. The driving circuitry can be quite simple and will not be discussed. This technology is quite well understood by motor manufacturers and need not be ex-plained here. The major subjects of this section are the motor and especially the mirror(s).

The available scan angle from a polygonal mirror of K facets can be shown to be,

$$\theta = \frac{720}{K} \quad \text{degrees} \tag{20}$$

This is so since the mirrors are on the circumference of a circle and if there are K mirrors, then each mirror must subtend $360/K$ degrees from the center of rotation. This equation does not apply when K has a value of 1 or 2 for obvious reasons. Furthermore, the scan angle is doubled by reflection as in galvanometers, giving $720/K$ as the scan angle per facet.

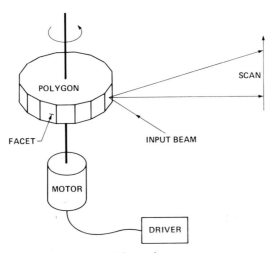

FIG. 13.   Polygonal scanner.

The minimum resolvable angle α given by Eq. (13) can be used to derive N_r for a polygonal scanner of K facets and facet width W. For a Gaussian beam, the relation,

$$N_r = 12.6 \frac{W}{\lambda K} \tag{21}$$

can be derived. For $W = 1$ cm, $K = 24$, and $\lambda = 633$ nm, Eq. (21) yields,

$$N_r = 8294 \quad \text{spots}$$

The merit function M, can be shown to be

$$M = 12.6 \frac{W}{K} \tag{22}$$

Substituting the above values into (22) the merit function is found to be,

$$M = 12.6 \times \frac{10}{24} = 5.24 \quad \text{mm}$$

This is a smaller merit function than that of the galvanometer cited before. Now, however, if we wish to make 6000 scans/sec from this device we need only spin the polygon at 6000/24 or 250 revolutions/sec. This is of course only 15000 rpm, which is not a stress on either the motor or the polygon, as we shall see. This scanner also produces ~8300 spots/scan. If we increase the number of facets to 36, the number of resolvable spots is ~3700 if the polygon diameter is kept approximately constant. This is about what we desire for our hypothetical printer, and the required rpm now reduces to 10,000, which is easier to achieve. For a reasonably large number of facets K the polygon diameter D is

$$D = \frac{WK}{\pi} \tag{23}$$

Thus our 36-facet polygon having 6.67-mm facets is only 76 mm or 3 in. in diam.

The polygonal scanner has some significant advantages over the galvanometer in that (1) it has multiple facets to reduce its rotational speed requirements, and (2) it moves only in one direction. The unidirectional characteristic of polygonal scanners should in general give them long life.

Until recently, there has been a severe problem with polygonal scanners that limited their volume producibility and cost effectiveness. This problem is the requirement of facet-to-facet angular uniformities. Assuming we wish to scan an 11-in. page with our 36-facet scanner, the system geometry requires a polygon-to-scan plane distance of ~31 in., as shown in Fig. 14. With the facet width W of 6.67 mm and a 31-in. or 787-mm polygon-to-scan plane distance D, the system $F/\#$ or focal ratio is,

$$F/\# = \frac{787}{6.67} = 118$$

If now we consider the facet to truncate the imaging beam so that it is uniformly illuminated, we can approximate the scan-spot size d as

$$d = 1.22\lambda(F/\#) \tag{24}$$

This equation is not strictly correct, since, due to the rectangular facet geometry, the spot size is really determined by a sinc^2 function rather than the square of a first-order Bessel function. The spot-size differences are minimal, however, and for the purposes of this discussion precise determination is not necessary. For $\lambda = 633$ nm, $d = 91$ μm or 3.6×10^{-3} in. at the 50% intensity points of the spot. The reader is left to work out the differences between the Gaussian, Bessel, and sinc function differences on spot shape, etc. In the author's experience, these differences are of only minor importance in general and are not considered here. Careful calculation and derivation of such spot-energy distributions are available from Born and Wolf (1964).

If we assume that we can tolerate a spot-position error of $\frac{1}{2}$ spot diameter at the 50% points, the allowable facet-to-facet angular error

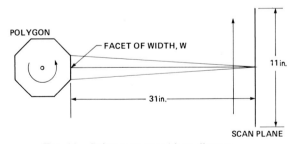

FIG. 14.   Polygon-to-scan plane diagram.

δ can be described as,

$$\delta = \frac{0.61\lambda(F/\#)}{D}$$

or   (25)

$$\delta = 58 \quad \mu\text{rad} \quad \text{or} \quad 12 \quad \text{arc-sec}$$

This angular error is the actual error that can be tolerated and since angles are doubled upon reflection from our mirrors, then δ must be halved to obtain the facet-to-facet tolerance value. This means that we can tolerate only ~6 arc-sec error between any two facets. Persons familiar with optical component fabrication will realize that this is difficult tolerance to achieve in production situations. Tolerances much tighter than this can be achieved in special devices, of course, but an actual commercial product cannot tolerate components costing many thousands of dollars each.

A technique must therefore be found to reduce the need for such precision fabrication. Schemes have been devised to sense the position of the scan beam at the image plane and use an acoustooptic deflector to "steer" the beam to the correct focal position. This, of course, complicates the optical system and reduces its overall efficiency, since another component has been introduced into the light path that has both transmission and reflection losses as well as diffraction efficiency losses. While space does not permit an extensive discussion of various techniques, optical correction schemes by the author (U.S. Patent #4,040,096) and also one by Fleischer (U.S. Patent #3,750,189) significantly reduce this problem. As shown in Fig. 15, a cylinder lens can be inserted into the optical path of the scanning beam to reduce the facet-to-facet angular tolerances by 50–100 times. This means that the angular tolerances can now be on the order of arc-minutes instead of arc-seconds, and the problem is sufficiently corrected to permit low-cost polygonal scanners to be used. It should be carefully noted by the reader that only polygon facet angular errors that produce ray deviations from the scan plane are corrected by the above technique.

The cylinder functions as follows: the polygon facet acts as the object for the cylinder lens and the lens therefore images the facet at an image plane that is intended to coincide with the photoreceptor surface. The image dimension in the vertical direction d_t (called the tangential direction), is therefore the dimension of the illuminated portion of the polygon facet multiplied by the magnification or minification of the optical system. If we define the illuminated height of the facet as A,

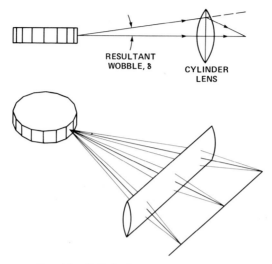

FIG. 15.   Cylinder-lens corrector.

the cylinder lens to facet distance O, and the cylinder lens to photo-receptor distance as I, then the tangential spot dimension is in the first order given by the relation,

$$d_t = \frac{AI}{O} \tag{26}$$

Thus, if we wish to have a final tangential spot size of ~0.1 mm at the 50% points and the facet-illuminated height is 1.0 mm, the system magnification should be 0.1×. Notice that if the facet is improperly positioned and causes the ray to deviate from a plane by some angle δ, the cylinder lens intercepts the ray and redirects it to the image scan line. This obviously corrects the effect of the facet error. Furthermore, this correction scheme is quite foolproof and not subject to malfunction. Further details can be obtained from U.S. Patent #4,040,096 discussed earlier.

With this simple correction scheme, the superior virtues of the polygonal scanner can now be exploited to the fullest with significant cost effectiveness. Although the first-order operation of this correction system is quite straightforward, actual systems must be carefully designed. While the majority of angular errors are to be found in the fabrication of the polygon, this system also corrects for bearing errors, etc. This is fortunate indeed since fabrication errors are quite stable with time and the motor bearings will gradually wear. Since in general this wear tends to look for all practical purposes like facet errors, the system corrects these as well. Bearing quality can also be relaxed since arc-second polygons require arc-second (class 9) bearings to make use of the fabrication precision. We shall now turn to the design character-istics of polygonal scanners for high-speed systems.

The polygonal scanner as mentioned earlier is basically a disk of material with optical flats on its periphery. When this optical element is rotated at high speed there are high stresses on the polygon material. Furthermore, the facets "paddle" the air and offer resistance to the rotating power source such as the motor.

These considerations need careful assessment in any high-speed printing system. Let us therefore consider the polygon requirements for a device printing an 11-in.-wide field and having a resolution of ~400 bits/in. and 400 scans/in. Furthermore, let us choose a photo-receptor velocity of 35 in./sec. The 35-in./sec photoreceptor velocity results in a printer capable of producing ~4 pages/sec. The foregoing specifications are well in excess of any device on the market today and can serve as an excellent test case for polygon scanner technology. This hypothetical printer would consume data at a *minimum* rate of 62×10^6 bits/sec. Let us now look at the resultant parameters of the polygon required to achieve this imaging task.

For this discussion, assume a polygon diameter of 3.0 in. or 76.2 mm. This permits the polygon to have 24 facets of ~1.0 cm each. Since our photoreceptor velocity is 35 in./sec and the scan density is 400 lines/in., the polygon must produce 14000 scans/sec. With 24 facets the polygon rotational rate is ~583 revolutions/sec or 35,000 rpm. A book by Schlichting (1968) called "Boundary Layer Theory" provides the following data for drag on rotating disks. The Reynolds number R is given by the relation

$$R = \frac{r^2\omega^2\rho}{\mu} \tag{27}$$

where r is the disk or polygon radius, ω is the disk angular velocity, ρ is the air density, and μ the air viscosity. We shall also define a coefficient C_m, which is related to the Reynolds number R by the re-lation,

$$C_m = \frac{3.87}{R^{1/2}} \tag{28}$$

which holds for a laminar flow region. This should be sufficient for our needs. The torque required to compensate for windage can be shown to be,

$$T = \frac{C_m \rho \omega^2 r^5}{2} \quad \text{oz.in.} \tag{29}$$

Last, the power required to overcome "the windage" losses can be shown to be,

$$P = \frac{TZ}{1351.75} \quad \text{W} \tag{30}$$

where Z is the rpm and the torque T is in ounce-inches. The units in (29) and (30) are purposely mixed since most motor specifications carry ounce-inch torque specifications rather than newton-meters. The reader should note that the coefficient C_m is dependent on many variables. If the polygon is enclosed in a tight enclosure for example, the constant changes from 3.87 to ~2.67, etc. Also, if turbulent flow is encountered the coefficient expression changes. For our purposes, however, let us assume Eq. (28) to be valid for this discussion.

The generally accepted value for the Reynolds number R at which transition from laminar to turbulent flow occurs is 3×10^5 as mentioned in Schlichting (1968). Also, the density of air ρ decreases with temperature and the kinematic viscosity μ increases. Substituting the appropriate values and constants, the Reynolds number is found to be 3.2×10^5, which is slightly above the laminar region. The torque T turns out to be 1.0 oz.-in. for a "free" or unenclosed polygon. The power therefore works out via Eq. (30) to be,

$$P = \frac{(1.0)(35,000)}{1351} = 26 \text{ W}$$

It is interesting to note that a printer running at half-speed (17.5 in./sec) with the other parameters the same as above requires an rpm of only 17,500. The Reynolds number turns out to be only 1.4×10^5. The resulting torque drops dramatically to 0.21 oz.-in. and the power decreases even more dramatically to 2.7 W! Thus the effect of windage losses can be relatively high, depending on rotor diameter and rpm. Should our scanner design require a rotor diameter of 4 in. instead of 3 in., for example, the power at 35,000 rpm is 100 W! This power loss is not, of course, just heat but can also result in significant "sirening." This noise must be damped out acoustically to prevent unwanted environmental disturbances. The more facets present on the disk periphery, the quieter the rotor since the apex joining the two facets does not project as far into the laminar or turbulent flow in the vicinity of the polygon surface. To some extent, the faceted nature of the polygon invalidates the disk approximation used in Eq. (29) earlier. The error introduced by the flat facets is in general not substantial, however.

The power losses discussed above are only for air-frictional effects. Motor bearings must also be considered as a source of friction. Whether one uses air bearings, grease bearings, or the more conventional ball bearings is a matter of tolerable service requirements, noise, and life.

Air bearings of course offer the quietest operation and the least power losses. A greased journal bearing would probably be the highest power consumer, but is also very "stiff" as compared to other bearing types. The scope of this article does not warrant a detailed discussion of bearing types. The reader is referred to Michalec (1966) and Meimel (1950) for more information on bearings, etc. It is sufficient to say that the range of power requirements for the various bearing types varies from a low of about 4 W for air bearings to a high of ~25 W for a grease journal bearing at our design rpm of 35,000.

The class of bearing or its precision will depend on how much the optical or electrooptic subsystem can tolerate facet "wobble." Rotor unbalance is very crucial as well with regard to vibration and bearing life. Our 3-in. polygon would generate an almost 4-lb side load if the rotor had only 10^{-3} oz.-in. of unbalance! Fortunately, balancing can be cost-effectively performed to much tighter tolerances than the above.

We must now look at the rotational stresses that our polygon undergoes while spinning in excess of 580 revolutions/sec. The disk periphery is moving at 458 ft/sec or ~Mach 0.5.

Since our polygon must be mounted to the driving motor via its shaft, a center bore in the polygon material must be provided. The polygon therefore becomes a spinning annulus. The stress on a spinning annulus can be shown to be,

$$S_t - (7.1 \times 10^{-6}) w Z^2 [(3 + m) R_o^2 + (1 - m) R_i^2] \qquad (31)$$

where w is the weight of the rotor material in pounds per cubic inch, Z is the rpm, R_o is the outer radius, R_i the inner radius, and m is Poisson's ratio. Equation (31) and the necessary data can be obtained from *Machinery's Handbook*, which is authored by Erik Oberg and Franklin D. Jones and is published by Industrial Press of New York.

Equation (31) can be solved for the rpm Z, at which the stress S_t equals the yield stress of the material being used. S_t is usually given in pounds. This would result in a maximum value of Z for the rotor parameters used. Assuming that $R_o^2 \gg R_i^2$ and making $m = 0.3$ (a good approximation), we can rewrite (31) as

$$Z_{max} = \left(\frac{4.27 \times 10^4 S_t}{wR_o^2} \right)^{1/2} \tag{32}$$

If we use the parameters for our ~3-in rotor, then we can generate a table comparing the performance of various materials. Such a comparison is shown in Table II. While mechanical finishing has a great deal to do with with the ability of rotating mechanisms to take loads, we can make some general conclusions here. Copper and brass, although easy materials to work with mechanically, provide poor spinner materials. Glass and stainless steel (#51430) are roughly identical. A polygon to meet our requirements could be made out of crown glass and still have a safety factor of about 2. Type 7075 Aluminum has the greatest margin of safety from among the practical materials considered. Our 24-facet polygon could produce about 1.7×10^8 spots/sec at maximum Z. Beryllium is marginally the best material from a polygon performance standpoint, being able to generate over 3×10^8 spots/sec (Zook, 1974). This material, however, has a high toxicity when machined and is also expensive. Beryllium is therefore dropped from discussion due to its general complications and expense, and it is clearly not necessary unless rpm's in excess of 70,000 ($2 \times$ safety factor) are

TABLE II

SELECTED POLYGON MATERIALS[a,b]

Material	Yield strength (psi)	Density (lb/in.³)	Poisson ratio	Maximum rpm
Aluminum 7075-T6	73,000	0.101	0.334	123,000
Stainless steel 51430	60,000	0.28	0.300	67,000
Copper	17,000	0.321	0.340	33,000
Brass	16,000	0.302	0.340	33,000
Glass	20,000	0.09	0.210	69,000
Beryllium	40,000	0.066	0.250	110,000

[a] Outer radius, 1.43 in.

[b] Inner radius, 0.25 in.

required. Actual surface profiles of the polygon mounting hole, e.g., make a great deal of difference in the ultimate rpm capabilities of the device. Our concern in an actual product is not usually the maximum attainable performance, but rather cost/performance.

The material that the polygon consists of should in general have a high strength-to-density ratio, low density, low Poisson's ratio, low thermal expansion coefficient, and be somewhat ductile and very stable. Depending on system requirements, there are several materials that can be used. Maximum performance and maximum cost are of course realized with exotic materials like beryllium. Various types of aluminum can be used to provide very good performance at acceptable prices.

As a last consideration for polygon scanners, we should concern ourselves with the rotation mechanism. Although one could drive the polygon from an air turbine, this might be unduly noisy. An electric motor is clearly best for the rpm regimes we are considering. There are many types of motors, of course, such as dc, induction, hysteresis-synchronous, etc. The system designer is left the task of selecting which motor technology best suits his needs. How the motor is driven, how the rpm is stabilized, etc., are all considerations that determine ultimate motor selection. The windage losses, bearing losses, and acceleration requirements will determine the ultimate power requirements of the polygon motor. Clearly the power requirements need not be very large for most practical systems, however.

In summary, the polygon deflector handles the laser-beam deflecting task very well. No particular aspect of either rotor or driver technology needs to be highly stressed to provide the required spots that our hypothetical 4-page/sec printer demands. While the future may well provide electrooptic or other successors to the polygon deflector, all current high-speed printing technologies use the multifaceted polygon as the prime beam-deflection mechanism.

VIII. Printer Optical Systems

We shall now proceed to discuss some of the characteristics of printer optical systems. This discussion will involve reference to the printer systems on the market today, viz, the Xerox 9700, IBM 3800, and Siemens ND-2. Detailed optical designs are not pertinent to the discussion here as space does not permit and the lens designs are not speed dependent in any case. The modulator and deflector are the main components affected by the data rate.

As referenced earlier, the printer optical systems are faced with producing small optical spots at a high rate. While the highest data rate available today is ~20 Mbits/sec (Xerox 9700), our hypothetical printer running at 400 bits/in.^{2} and ~4 pages/sec consumes data at 60 + Mbits/sec. We have seen the modulator and polygon characteristics that are required for this performance level. We shall also look at the optical system light throughput to achieve the required exposure at a photoreceptor velocity of 35 in./sec. The next section on the xerographic subsystem will deal with the elements of xerographic systems as they pertain to our printing tasks.

A. IBM 3800

The IBM 3800 was the first high-speed laser printer to be introduced to the marketplace. It was announced in April 1975 and deliveries to customers began in approximately the third quarter of 1976. The scan density in this unit is not square. The bit density along the direction of scan is 180 bits/in. and the scan line density is 144 scans/in. The printer is capable of producing copy up to 14 in. wide and the photoconductor drum moves at approximately 31 in./sec. Thus there are ~2632 bits/scan and ~4464 scans/second that result in a data rate of approximately 11.8×10^6 bits/sec. The bit time is therefore ~85 nsec. With operational duty cycles considered, as discussed later, the actual spot time is about 75 nsec.

A drawing of the optical system is shown in Fig. 16. Light from the laser passes through a beam "compressor" that forms a spot or beam waist that is approximately $\frac{1}{3}$ of the diameter of the beam exiting the laser. This reduced beam size permits the modulator rise time to be much shorter as a result of the reduced transit time of the acoustic wave, as discussed in the section on modulators. The beam then expands as it exits the modulator and goes to an expander lens, which reconditions the beam for its entrance to the first cylindrical lens. This first cylindrical lens has its power plane oriented orthogonal to the direction of scan. A "knife-edge" stop is used to "trap" or stop the zero-order modulator beam, since only the first or diffracted order is desired for data writing. The entire diffracted laser beam then impinges on the polygon facet, which redirects the beam via the scanning motion

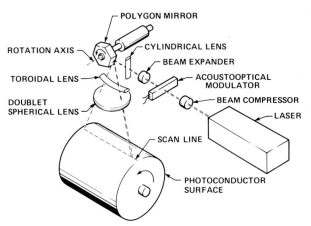

FIG. 16.   IBM 3800 optical diagram.

to a toroidal lens and a final spherical lens. A detailed description of the system is given in Fleischer *et al.* (1977).

The beam-compressor and beam-expander optics are actually composed of four lenses. The optical system utilizes a correction technique similar to the one described earlier to reduce the polygon angular fabrication requirements significantly. The laser is approximately 1 m in length and is of the He–Ne type. Because of its power output level the laser is rated Class III. Appropriate interlocking of the system permits Class I operation. Additionally, the laser must be in a temperature controlled environment and is required to produce nearly constant output power over a temperature range of about 20°C.

The polygon facets must be several times larger than the impinging beam for adequate duty-cycle operation. This is more clearly illustrated in Fig. 17. Here the beam of diameter d, falls upon the facet of width W. Actual printing of information cannot begin until the entire beam is on the facet surface. Furthermore, printing must cease when any further rotation of the polygon would truncate the beam at the end of the scan. This means that the facet can only move through a distance $W - d$ for full beam scanning to be possible. Thus the duty cycle U is shown to be,

$$U = (W - d)/W \qquad (33)$$

If the facet width W is 10 times the beam diameter d, then the duty cycle U becomes 90%. This means that the modulator bandwidth must be increased 10%, since only 90% of the available time is used for printing. This 10% "dead time" can be thought of as retrace or fly-back in the television sense, but the optical beam does not physically fly back, it just starts over. Systems utilizing this scanning technique must be carefully designed to avoid large polygon size and unduly high rotational speed.

For example, if the beam diameter at the polygon is 3 mm, then a 90% duty cycle would require a 30-mm facet. A polygon having 15 such facets would be nearly 15 cm or 6 in. in diameter. The rpm Z would also have to be ~18,000. A little reflection on the polygon design parameters in the previous section will permit the reader to determine the high stresses on such a device even at this moderate speed. Keeping polygon diameter small and duty cycle high is a necessary and challenging system design problem for high-speed printer systems. A valuable and noteworthy illustration of the effect of facet "wobble" both corrected and uncorrected is shown in Fleischer *et al.* (1977).

One portion of the optical system in the IBM 3800 that is not shown is the so-called forms overlay optics. The optical subsystem is not part of the laser scan unit and uses a xenon flash lamp and optical system to image a full-form negative transparency onto the xerographic drum. This subsystem will be described in a later section dealing with the printer as a whole.

B. SIEMENS ND-2/3352

The Siemens ND-2 is the latest printer to become available in the marketplace and is discussed here because of some similarities to the

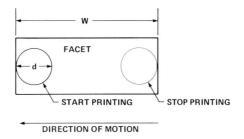

FIG. 17. Polygon-facet duty-cycle $[U = (W - d)/W]$ diagram.

IBM 3800 unit. This printer is also called the Siemens 3352 printer in later literature. Itel in the United States markets this unit which is of course manufactured in Germany. The printer has nearly the same throughput as the IBM 3800. The scanning resolutions are also identical (180 × 144). This represents 25,920 resolution elements/in.[2]

Less is known about Siemens 3352 printer than either the IBM 3800 or the Xerox 9700, since less has been published concerning its technical details. The principal difference between the 3352 and the 3800 is in the optical system for scanning and the forms projection. Again, the forms projection will be discussed later, along with the overall printer performance specifications. Figure 18 illustrates the Siemens 3352 printer optical schematic. This system is novel in that, although a polygon is used for the main deflection task, an acoustooptic deflector is used in conjunction with this polygon to produce a small vertical raster orthogonal to the main direction of scan.

As shown in Fig. 18 the light from the laser again passes through some beam-forming optics and the properly conditioned beam enters an acoustooptic deflector. This component also functions as a modulator, although no detailed data is available as to how this is actually accomplished in the 3352. It is likely that a technique similar to that described by Meye (1977) is used in this printer, even though no specific reference to the 3352 is given. The unit no doubt functions like a multibeam modulator. The laser beam then passes to an imaging lens that is placed before the 14-faceted polygonal scanner. How wobble correction is achieved is not stated. The small vertical raster that is generated can however, be used to correct for beam displacements if sensing of the beam position at the image surface or plane can be monitored and fed to the deflection electronics. The light from the imaging lens passes to the polygon and on to the xerographic drum for image printing. The significance of the multibeam acoustooptic deflector is that since six lines are generated simultaneously, the polygon rotational velocity can be slowed considerably. As we shall see later, the character lines are 24-scan lines high and thus four scans are required to complete a character line. This is crucial for a polygon that must be large to achieve resonable duty cycle in this optical configuration. Since the process speed of the 3352 is approximately the same as the 3800, a 14-facet polygon would have to rotate at ~19,000 rpm if the vertical deflector were not used. The vertical deflector reduces this speed to ~3200 rpm, which is modest indeed. The acoustooptic deflector must accept data at a rate of about 15 Mbits/sec. The light beam is focussed

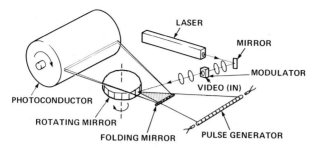

FIG. 18. Siemens 3352 printer optical diagram.

to 0.25 mm or 0.01 in. For image smoothness (especially in angled patterns) the dots overlap highly. This is so since the reciprocal spot diameter is 100/in. and the actual scan density in the direction of scan is 180/in. (Kuchenbecker and Unger, 1977).

The Siemens 3352 printer represents an interesting printing device which, while similar in resolution and architecture to the IBM 3800, has some novel technical variations. The performance of this printer and similar units in the marketplace will be a fascinating study.

C. XEROX 9700

The Xerox 9700 optical system is the last to be discussed since it is architecturally different from the IBM and Siemens devices. Furthermore, the 9700 resolution is considerably in excess of the other two devices, being 300/in.^{2} This means that the 9700 produces 90,000 dots/in.^{2} instead of 25,920 for the other two printers. Additionally, the 9700 prints only 11-in. wide and forms are printed digitally with the characters. This eliminates the forms overlay or flash systems used in the other two printers.

As shown in Fig. 19, the light from the laser proceeds to some beam-"conditioning" optics that focus the light for appropriate modulator rise-time performance. The laser in this case is a He–Cd type of proprietary design. This unit permits a non-red-sensitive photoreceptor to be used and actually the xerographic marking engine is derived from the Xerox 9200 copier/duplicator machine. Again, this engine and some of its xerographic details will be discussed later. The He–Cd laser has a power output of about 10–15 mW. While the He–Cd laser technology is more complicated than that for He–Ne, there are some peripheral benefits such as a larger permissible imaging $f/\#$ for the same desired

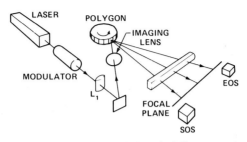

FIG. 19.   Xerox 9700 optical diagram.

image spot size, etc. These benefits do not warrant choosing He–Cd
over He–Ne, however. The 9700 uses the He–Cd laser to utilize the
9200 marking-engine technology.

The light from the modulator passes to a cylinder lens whose power
plane is oriented orthogonal to the direction of scan and then to a
spherical lens. The light then is reflected by the polygon, onto the
correction lens, and from there to the photoreceptor. The first cylinder
lens (pre-polygon), spherical lens, and correction lens form an anamorphic imaging system. This anamorphic imaging system is intended
to produce a spot at the photoreceptor that is very close to round. The
advantage of the anamorphic system is that component separation can
be realized, and some significant polygon advantages can be obtained.
One principal advantage is that in this optical system more than one
facet is illuminated. In fact nearly three are simultaneously illuminated.
Figure 20 illustrates this situation.

As the figure shows, the scanning facet moves through a field or line
of light. Thus the entire facet width does the imaging. The duty cycle
is very high since the facet is illuminated during its entire scan traversal.
Typical scan duty cycles are 90% and higher in practice. This technique
is obviously wasteful of light but xerographic sensitivity is tolerant of
this one architectual drawback. The principal advantage is that the
polygon turns out to be quite small. For example, if the spot size is
chosen to be ~0.003 in. or 76 μm at the 50% points then the required
$F \#$ for the He–Cd wavelength of 442 nm is ~140 as determined from
Eq. (24). Thus if the the polygon-to-scan plane distance is ~35 in. the
required facet width would be,

$$W = \frac{35}{140} = 0.25 \quad \text{in.}$$

The scan angle required for an 11-in. scan line to be produced by a 35-in. polygon-to-scan-plane distance calculated to be ~18°. If we use a 36-facet polygon, then by Eq. (20), the maximum scan angle is found to be 20°. Thus a 36-facet polygon would have a scan efficiency of 90% (18°/20°) and be only 2.86 in. in diameter. The multiplicity of facets also means that at the 9700 process speed 20 in./sec, an rpm of only 10,000 is required. This is very straightforward with this size of polygon.

Also shown in Fig. 19 is the start-of-scan detector. This detector senses the scan beam prior to its passage onto the appropriate area of the photosensitive surface. Since the digital data buffer must be "triggered" or "clocked" synchronously with the optical writing beam, some form of beam-position detection is necessary. The 9700 system uses a separate detector for this purpose. This detector should be a "fast" system, since in the case of the 9700, the bits time is ~50 nsec. For a synchronization start precision of $\frac{1}{4}$ bit, the detector must have an optically and electronically precise rise time of ~12 nsec. This is non-trivial in general. As shown in Fig. 21, a detector having two sensitive areas separated by a small non-light-sensitive boundary can be used for this purpose. The detector areas are electrically separate and logically connected in such a way that each detector is enabled only when light is on either one. Additionally, each detector feeds into one of two inputs of a comparator. The detector being illuminated first is connected to the comparator reference with the second detector connected to the signal side. The comparator will switch or deliver a pulse at the point where the detectors are equally illuminated, i.e., the boundary. This scheme is also positionally stable with respect to intensity fluctuations since light *equality*, not intensity, is sensed for triggering purposes. Very fast comparators can be obtained using devices fabricated

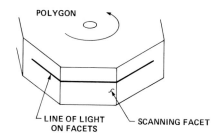

FIG. 20.   Xerox 9700 facet-illumination scheme.

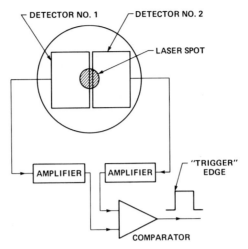

FIG. 21.   Dual start of scan detector.

from emitter-coupled logic (ECL). These devices have rise times of less than 2 nsec and switch on 1- or 2-mV differences.

Typically, silicon photodiodes can be used for the detection apparatus. At the He–Ne wavelength of 633 nm, silicon photodiodes have a sensitivity of ~0.6 A/W. Thus if the laser writing beam has a power of ~1 mW, then the the signal across a 50-Ω load resistor would be ~30 mV. This is more than adequate to drive an appropriately designed amplifier and subsequently the comparator. This scheme is not the only way in which to scan detect and trigger, but is presented as a workable scheme that is used on the 9700 printer. The IBM 3800 also uses a scan detector for data- and writing-beam synchronization.

The optical system efficiencies are of course important to these printers. Light is not free and at the speeds the printers operate, the drum exposure demands care in system design efficiency. We can do some comparisons by modeling a simple optical scanning system and observing its overall efficiency. As shown in Fig. 22, we have a typical scanning system. This system is composed of the laser, two pre-modulator lenses for beam "conditioning," the modulator, three more imaging lenses, and the polygon. We should also consider at least three mirrors of reflectance R. Considering the transmission of each lens in the system to be T, the mirror reflectance losses R, the modulator net diffraction efficiency E, and the polygon efficiency including configurational losses to be P, the net system efficiency S, is

$$S = T^5R^3EP \tag{34}$$

Letting the average lens transmittance T and mirror reflectance R equal 0.93, and the modulator efficiency equal 0.8, the value of S is given by

$$S = (0.93)^8(0.8)P = 0.45P$$

It is interesting to note that if the average component transmittance/reflectance is equal to only 0.9, the value of S drops to $0.34P$, or 24% less light throughput. If the polygon efficiency is 0.4, as in the 9700, then S equals ~20%. Compared to the polygon efficiency of an estimated 0.9 in the 3800 and 3352 printers, which yields an S of 41%, the 9700 efficiency is less than half. This is more than offset by the sensitivity of the xerographic photoreceptor in the 9700. This photoreceptor needs less than 10 ergs/cm^2 for the required exposure. The 3800 and 3352 printers require an estimated 30–40 ergs/cm.^{2} Thus the 9700 system can tolerate a less efficient system because of its more sensitive xerographic photoreceptor. These variations represent rather interesting design trade-offs.

If we now wish to compare the actual laser power required for exposure, we can use the following relation:

$$P_1 = \frac{qA}{S} \tag{35}$$

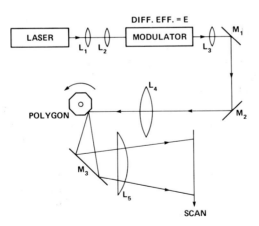

FIG. 22.   Optical system radiometric model.

where P_1 is the required laser power, q is the required exposure, A is the area written per unit time, and S is the system efficiency. The amount of area exposed by the 3800 laser subsystem is determined by the scan width of 37.1 cm and photoreceptor velocity of $\sim$79 cm/sec. Using this area exposure rate of 2900 cm^2/sec, and assuming the value of q for the 3800 to be 30 ergs/cm^2 the value of P_1 turns out to be

$$P_1 = \frac{(3 \times 10^{-6})(2.9 \times 10^3)}{0.41} = 21 \quad \text{mW}$$

The 9700 calculation would become

$$P_1 = \frac{(10^{-6})(1.4 \times 10^3)}{0.2} = 7 \quad \text{mW}$$

Of course the lasers actually used must have more power than this, since some margin for system efficiency deterioration, laser aging, and other losses must be allowed for. The point to be remembered here is that significant printing rates are supported by relatively small lasers, regardless of the printer chosen.

To summarize, the optical systems used in the printers discussed are not particularly complicated. This simplicity is a result of careful design and, unless absolutely necessary, complication should be suspect. We shall now proceed to the overall printer configurations and performance for a discussion of the system as a whole including the xerographic marking subsystem.

IX. Printer Systems

Now that the laser subsystem and component technologies have been generally reviewed, we can look at the printer as a whole. The general xerographic and paper path configurations as well as image performance are important considerations. The user is usually not very concerned about the actual technology used, only in the overall ability of the printer to satisfy his needs in a cost-effective manner. There are printers that use electrographic technology such as the Honeywell PPS (Page Printing System). This unit is fast, but runs at lower resolution levels than the laser scan printers we are discussing. Also, for better or worse, electrographic printers require special coated paper to retain the applied electrostatic charge until development occurs. Low-to-medium-speed printers can be obtained from companies such as Versatec, Varian, Gould, etc. The Honeywell PPS system is the only system that is in the same throughput league with our high-speed laser units.

A. IBM 3800

A diagram of the IBM 3800 printer system is shown in Fig. 23. For those readers interested in printer details, the article by Vahtra and Wolter (1978) is very useful as an extensive review of the 3800 control, xerography, etc. (Additionally, a 1978 article by Wolter may be useful.) Referring to Fig. 23, it can be seen that the laser subsystem is mounted at the bottom of the machine and exposes the drum at approximately the 8 o'clock position. The photoconductor drum is composed of a drum with an opening shown at the 12 o'clock position in Fig. 23. The photoconductor is wrapped around the drum. After several thousand images are made, the photoconductor is changed. This changing occurs by feeding fresh photoconductor from the supply spool to the take-up spool in the interior of the drum, similar to a scroll.

The xerographic subsystem operation is much the same, whether we are concerned with the Xerox 9700, IBM 3800, or Siemens 3352, and

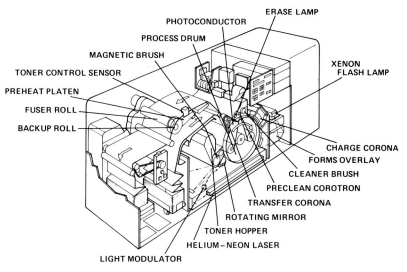

FIG. 23.   IBM 3800 printer.

hence only one basic process flow is described here. The photoconductor is charged at the charge station. This initial charge is about 750 V. The charging device is a multiwire scorotron, which is similar to a series of wires that have a screen wire or wires to limit maximum photoconductor charge potential. With a He–Ne exposure of ~30–40 ergs/cm^2, the charge is reduced to ~200 V. This means that the electrostatic contrast would be 550 V. The exposed photoconductor moves to a forms flash station, where a xenon flash unit images the transparent form by near-contact exposure. The photoconductor then moves to the laser exposure station and then to the development zone, where the image is developed. The developed image moves to the transfer station, where the web of paper receives the image. The drum then moves on to an erase lamp zone, which discharges the remaining unexposed areas of the drum. Last, the drum moves to a cleaning zone, where a rotating cleaning brush, combined with vacuum, removes residual toner from the photoconductor surface. The cycle is now complete and the drum can be recharged for repeated imaging. Both the IBM and Siemens printers use "negative" or discharge-area xerography. The Xerox 9700 uses charged-area or "positive" development. In negative xerography, the image areas to be developed (turned black) are exposed. The xerographic system electrostatics cause the toner to be deposited on the noncharged or exposed zones. In positive xerography, image areas to be developed are left unexposed and the toner is attracted to the charged or image zones. Each process has its advantages. In the 3800 and Siemens printers, forms flash or overlay would not be possible without negative development. Images can be effectively "added" in discharge-area development, whereas this is impossible in positive xerography. Positive xerography is of course most commonly used in xerographic copiers of all types, since the "originals" themselves are usually positive. We shall see in the 9700 discussion how the Xerox unit copes with forms generation and reproduction.

After transfer the paper moves to the fuser section for heat fusing of the toner image. The paper then moves on to the stacker. Optional equipment on the printer includes a burster–stacker–trimmer (BST) for handling the high-speed printer output. The process occurs at ~80 cm/sec or ~31 in./sec. The characters are created via an 18 × 24 dot matrix. A control system monitors the printer operation and controls the timing and imaging functions. Again, additional control and xerographic detail is available in Vahtra and Wolter (1978).

The use of fanfold paper was chosen because of user surveys and related design studies according to IBM. Web or fanfold paper has both advantages and disadvantages from a system design standpoint. Some advantages of fanfold or web paper are the degree of control that the system has on the paper feeding and positioning, as well as the diminished productivity loss due to intersheet gaps in sheet feeding. Cut-sheet paper is more difficult to handle as far as feeding and jam control are concerned. Web paper systems also have some important disadvantages. Some of these disadvantages are skewing and/or wrinkled sheets. Paper-path alignment is more crucial in a web system since force differentials along the paper width cause unbalances. These unbalances are communicated mechanically backward along the paper web and can cause the paper to poorly contact the photoconductor surface at the transfer point. The result is skips and/or smears. This effect can also occur in cut-sheet printers but is obviously less of a problem. The 3800 also must provide for lifting the paper transfer mechanism as well as stopping the paper while the drum gap passes underneath.

The result of all the foregoing subsystems is a printer that generates output at the rate of 13,360 lines/min. A line of type or output is usually 120 characters wide but can range usually from 80 to 132. Also, the number of characters per line is dependent on the character size or pitch. Depending on character size, the 3800 can print up to 45,000 characters/sec. This is nearly six times faster than any IBM impact printer. While the speed of laser printers is impressive, the reader should realize that nonimpact printers produce only *one* page per imaging pass. An impact printer can produce up to approximately 6 because carbon-paper forms or paper can be used. This means that in general a nonimpact printer must be faster to realize the same productivity as impact systems. Mulitpart paper and form usage profiles are crucial in deciding whether a nonimpact unit makes sense from this perspective. While a nonimpact printer, such as the 3800, 3352, and 9700, cannot create multipart forms at once as an impact printer is capable of doing, each copy is identical in quality. This is clearly not so with impact devices.

Another significant advantage of the above nonimpact printer technologies is font flexibility, Many different fonts are available on the 3800, such as Gothic 10 and 12, OCR A and B, graphic fonts, etc. Four fonts/page are permitted and fonts can be specially designed. Upper and lower case represent two fonts. Recently, IBM announced software for graphics that is specially useful in business applications. Additionally. custom-character-design assistance is available. The character generator is described in Vahtra and Wolter (1978), but basically consists of four Writable Character Generation Modules or WCGMs. These modules are controlled by character address (A, B, etc.) as well as character position.

The character generator permits a 6-bit character code or 64 characters. A character-generator buffer module supplies data to the WCGMs. The WCGM output goes to an output data register and 9-bit serializer, which is coupled to the laser-system modulator. There also are 64-graphic characters stored internal to the system. Format control, allowing mixing of different lines per inch, as well as intermixing of character pitches, on a text or print line, is permitted.

The IBM 3800 represents a modern technology, high-speed, non-impact printer that produces output at the rate of ~150 ft/min. This system sells for about $310,000 and is obviously not inexpensive. If a user needs its capabilities, however, and generates sufficient print volume to make reasonable use of such a device, it is a cost-effective system that reaches well beyond the capabilities of conventional impact printers.

B. SIEMENS ND-2/3352

The Siemens 3352 is xerographically similar to the IBM 3800 in that it uses web paper and the photoconductor is mounted to a drum. As shown in Fig. 24, the printer has the laser subsystem mounted at the side of the xerographic drum, with the exposure occurring at approximately the 4 o'clock position. Drum rotational direction is identical (clockwise) to the 3800. As the diagram indicates, the drum is charged by a corotron assembly. This assembly is similar to the scorotron, except that no screen wires are present to limit maximum drum charge. There are no unusual xerographic stations in the system. The system uses discharge area development similar to the 3800. The drum does not use scrolled photoreceptor material, however. This eliminates the need for raising the paper web and stopping it when the drum "gap" passes underneath. The paper transfer zone does have the capability of being raised however, so that when the drum is started up for printing the paper can be accelerated to the required velocity and then brought into contact with the drum. Also, should data flow be interrupted, the paper is raised and stopped. The start-up process repeats when printing is to be resumed.

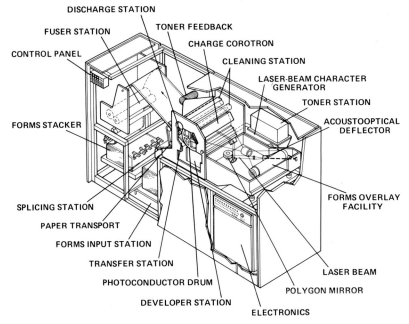

FIG. 24.   Siemens 3352 printer.

The forms exposure station is of the drum scan variety. A lens images the transparent negative form onto the drum prior to laser exposure. The form overlay can be up to 13.8 in. in length (350 mm) and the height can be a maximum of 13 in. (330 mm). Usable paper weights are 13–27 lb fanfold stock. The paper must be single part only. The paper feeder can hold about 4000 sheets. Printer power requirements are approximately 10 kVA.

The character generator produces characters having an 18 × 24 dot matrix, as in the 3800. As with the 3800, a number of fonts are available. The photoreceptor drum runs at approximately 74 cm/sec. With a line spacing of 12 lines/in., 21,000 lines of information can be printed per minute. The printer produces about 146 pages/min with 12-in. forms. Simple graphics can be printed with the 3352, and character overprinting is also permitted. This permits special language and scientific notations to be more readily printed.

Printer control and image generation are performed via a microprocessor and 4 kbytes of microprogram memory (8 bits/byte). Data format and memory consists of 32 kbytes standard with 32 kbytes optional. As discussed earlier, the most novel aspect of this printer is that it produces a scan six dots or scan lines high at a time.

The Siemens printer is an interesting and novel entry into the high-speed laser printer market. The unit is quite small, occupying only ~25 ft^2 of floor area and is slightly less than 6 ft in height. Selling price is estimated at ~$250,000. It is presumed to be available on an OEM basis but the exact price is as yet unknown. Itel is currently marketing this Siemens unit in the United States.

C. Xerox 9700

The Xerox 9700 was introduced at the National Computer Conference in June of 1977. Actual deliveries of this printer system began in mid-1978. The 9700 is architecturally quite different from the two printers discussed previously. For this reason we shall look a little more into the system details of this device. Maximum printer line rate is 18,000 lines/min. The xerographic system is taken from the Xerox Corporation's high-speed 9200 copier/duplicator unit. The announced selling price of the 9700 is ~$300,000. Printing is done at a maximum width of 11 in.

As shown in Fig. 25, the photoreceptor is in a flexible belt configuration. This belt passes around three rollers as it turns counterclockwise. The photoreceptor velocity is 20 in./sec. As shown in the figure, charging is performed by a corotron. The laser beam then writes the image onto the photoreceptor belt. The exposed image is then developed and transferred at the topmost portion of the belt. One major system difference from the 3800 and 3352 printers is the use of cut-sheet paper. This provides some major system advantages, as we shall soon see. The individual sheets of paper move along the top of the machine from one of two paper supplies at the rear of the machine.

As discussed earlier, the image in the 9700 is written for charged-area xerographic development. Thus instead of characters being written by the laser beam, all the area around the characters is discharged. The printer runs at a resolution of 300 bits/in. or 90,000 bits/in.^{2} This increased resolution, combined with the sophisticated character generator, allows the forms to be produced *digitally* instead of optically. The text and forms are thus combined as a video stream for subsequent laser modulation. This has the advantage of permitting precollation of

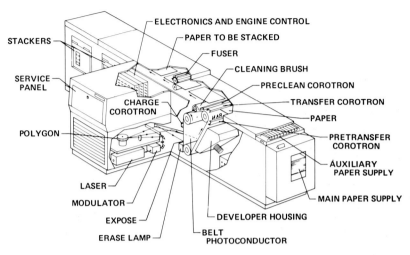

FIG. 25. Xerox 9700 printer.

the document or report to be printed. Approximately 800 pages can be stored on the system magnetic disk. Form quality can be quite high. Figure 26 illustrates a portion of a form produced on the 9700. Pre-printed forms used in web printers do not permit convienient changing since the web must be rethreaded for each change. Even overlay forms printing lacks the flexibility of digital forms generation. An illustration of a typical digital character is shown in Fig. 27. Each small square or "bit" comprising the character in Fig. 27 is approximately 0.0033 in. on a side (300 bits/in.).

As stated previously, paper is supplied from one of two locations. The first or main paper tray holds 2500 sheets of paper (20 lb). This sheet capacity, is of course, dependent on paper basis weight, since this corresponds to paper thickness. Paper weight can range from 16–110 lb card stock. The various paper weights can be intermixed in the paper supply. No machine adjustments are required for a change in paper weight. Since the printer runs at 120 sheets per min, the main tray is adequate for approximately 20 min running time. An auxiliary tray holding 400 sheets is also resident at the right end of the machine above the main paper supply. This can be used as a running tray while reloading the main tray or, under system control, sheets can be fed from this tray for document printing. This is especially useful for producing covers, etc. Since the forms and variable information can be

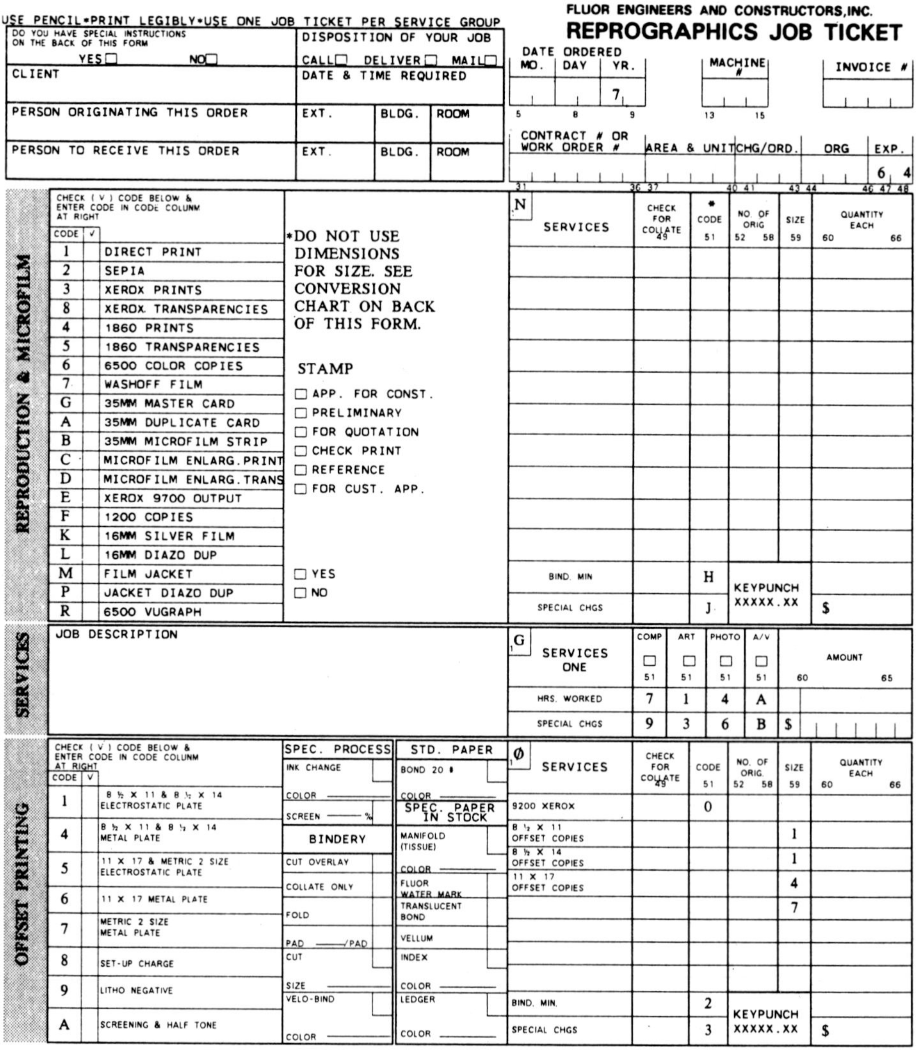

USE PENCIL•PRINT LEGIBLY•USE ONE JOB TICKET PER SERVICE GROUP

FLUOR ENGINEERS AND CONSTRUCTORS,INC.

REPROGRAPHICS JOB TICKET

DO YOU HAVE SPECIAL INSTRUCTIONS ON THE BACK OF THIS FORM	DISPOSITION OF YOUR JOB
YES☐ NO☐	CALL☐ DELIVER☐ MAIL☐
CLIENT	DATE & TIME REQUIRED

DATE ORDERED			MACHINE #	INVOICE #
MO.	DAY	YR.		
		7		
5	8	9	13 15	

PERSON ORIGINATING THIS ORDER	EXT.	BLDG.	ROOM
PERSON TO RECEIVE THIS ORDER	EXT.	BLDG.	ROOM

CONTRACT # OR WORK ORDER #	AREA & UNIT	CHG/ORD.	ORG	EXP.
31 36 37	40 41	43 44	46 47	6 4 48

REPRODUCTION & MICROFILM

CHECK (✔) CODE BELOW & ENTER CODE IN CODE COLUMN AT RIGHT

CODE	✔	
1		DIRECT PRINT
2		SEPIA
3		XEROX PRINTS
8		XEROX TRANSPARENCIES
4		1860 PRINTS
5		1860 TRANSPARENCIES
6		6500 COLOR COPIES
7		WASHOFF FILM
G		35MM MASTER CARD
A		35MM DUPLICATE CARD
B		35MM MICROFILM STRIP
C		MICROFILM ENLARG. PRINT
D		MICROFILM ENLARG. TRANS
E		XEROX 9700 OUTPUT
F		1200 COPIES
K		16MM SILVER FILM
L		16MM DIAZO DUP
M		FILM JACKET
P		JACKET DIAZO DUP
R		6500 VUGRAPH

•DO NOT USE DIMENSIONS FOR SIZE. SEE CONVERSION CHART ON BACK OF THIS FORM.

STAMP

☐ APP. FOR CONST.
☐ PRELIMINARY
☐ FOR QUOTATION
☐ CHECK PRINT
☐ REFERENCE
☐ FOR CUST. APP.

☐ YES
☐ NO

N	SERVICES	CHECK FOR COLLATE 49	CODE 51	NO. OF ORIG. 52 58	SIZE 59	QUANTITY EACH 60 66
	BIND. MIN		H	KEYPUNCH XXXXX.XX		
	SPECIAL CHGS		J			$

SERVICES

JOB DESCRIPTION

G	SERVICES ONE	COMP 51	ART 51	PHOTO 51	A/V 51		AMOUNT 60 65
		☐	☐	☐	☐		
	HRS. WORKED	7	1	4	A		
	SPECIAL CHGS	9	3	6	B	$	

OFFSET PRINTING

CHECK (✔) CODE BELOW & ENTER CODE IN CODE COLUMN AT RIGHT

CODE	✔	
1		8 ½ X 11 & 8 ½ X 14 ELECTROSTATIC PLATE
4		8 ½ X 11 & 8 ½ X 14 METAL PLATE
5		11 X 17 & METRIC 2 SIZE ELECTROSTATIC PLATE
6		11 X 17 METAL PLATE
7		METRIC 2 SIZE METAL PLATE
8		SET-UP CHARGE
9		LITHO NEGATIVE
A		SCREENING & HALF TONE

SPEC. PROCESS	
INK CHANGE	
COLOR _____	
SCREEN _____ %	
	BINDERY
CUT OVERLAY	
COLLATE ONLY	
FOLD	
PAD _____/PAD	
CUT	
SIZE	
VELO-BIND	
COLOR _____	

STD. PAPER	
BOND 20 #	
COLOR _____	
SPEC. PAPER IN STOCK	
MANIFOLD (TISSUE)	
COLOR _____	
FLUOR WATER MARK	
TRANSLUCENT BOND	
VELLUM	
INDEX	
COLOR _____	
LEDGER	
COLOR _____	

Ø	SERVICES	CHECK FOR COLLATE 49	CODE 51	NO. OF ORIG. 52 58	SIZE 59	QUANTITY EACH 60 66
	9200 XEROX		0			
	8 ½ X 11 OFFSET COPIES				1	
	8 ½ X 14 OFFSET COPIES				1	
	11 X 17 OFFSET COPIES				4	
					7	
	BIND. MIN.		2	KEYPUNCH XXXXX.XX		
	SPECIAL CHGS		3			$

FIG. 26.   Xerox 9700 form example.

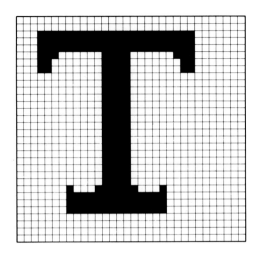

Fɪɢ. 27. Xerox 9700 32 × 32 bit character matrix.

printed at once, complete reports are producible including the covers if the user so desires.

The 9700 has two stacker modules at the left or copy-delivery end of the machine. Each stacker holds 1500 sheets of paper (20 lb). The printing runs are offset and stacked so that job and/or copy separation is convienient upon job completion. Additionally, when one stacker is full, the output switches to the second, so that unloading can occur on the first, and so forth. There is also a provision for copy previewing should the operator or user wish to see a sample of what they are printing. The operator merely requests a sample and it is delivered into a sample print tray at the top of the leftmost stacker. This obviates the need for waiting until current job completion occurs. This is one of the benefits of cut-sheet operation. Web-fed devices require continuity of pages to simplify the bursting operation.

The 9200 xerographic engine flow path is such that the entire image is created on the xerographic belt prior to the need for sheet commitment from the paper tray. This means that should an image-creation fault be detected during the exposing process, the sheet of paper that would receive the image can be held up and the image reprinted. This eliminates the need for capturing known defective images. This is again not possible with web or fanfold devices.

A system diagram is shown in Fig. 28. The printer uses a rigid disk to store system information, files, and character-matrix information. A PDP 11/34 computer handles the system management tasks and provides control of the character generator for disk and printer control requirements. Space does not warrant a detailed discussion of the character generator, but we can review some of the pertinent performance capabilities of this system.

The 9700 unit is available with on-line and off-line interfaces. The system is supplied in standard form with four 64-character sets but can be extended to provide up to twelve 128-character sets/page. This permits significant page complexity. Print format is variable from 3 to 18 lines/in. vertically. Character point sizes from 4 to 24 points are permitted. Page density for variable data is 9900 characters in the basic system and can be extended to 19,800/page. This of course permits a maximum character rate of 39,600 characters/sec since 2 pages/sec are produced. The printer handles many host–system interfaces.

The 9700 represents an interesting technology since, while it is capable of emulating a line printer, it clearly has far more capabilities. How these capabilities will be used in practice remains to be observed, but its potential for high-quality electronic-image generation is obvious. The elimination of the need for storage of preprinted forms also eliminates costly overhead in many applications. Specific applications will obviously determine the utility and cost/effectiveness of these features.

Just recently, two additional 9700 system capabilities were announced by Xerox. The first system introduced, designated the 817 Fiche Subsystem, provides the capability to produce complete CRT-

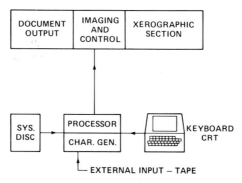

FIG. 28.   Xerox 9700 system diagram.

generated microfiche from the 9700 electronic subsystem. The 817 subsystem produces cut fiche ready for distribution. Reduction ratios are $42\times$ standard with each recorder processor, with $24\times$ and $48\times$ reductions optional. All of the 9700 forms-generation capabilities, as well as font sizes and styles, are available to the 817 microfiche user. The second system capability introduced in June 1979 is a duplex printing feature. This feature permits printing on both sides of the paper under system control. Thus, two-sided printing capability previously available only in general on copiers, now is available on this high-speed laser printing system.

The cost/effectiveness of printer systems, especially nonimpact units, depends on many factors. Often the technologist feels that the use of a "laser" in the printer is exotic enough to justify the end cost. The data-processing manager or end user, however, usually cares little about the technology his printer uses, so long as it is reliable, provides the features needed or desired, and is a net cost benefit over competing opportunities. High-speed printers are most cost effective when used at high volume. Also, precollation helps to greatly reduce the finishing costs. Software forms available on the 3800, 3352, or 9700 help to reduce the finishing task and may greatly reduce paper cost by eliminating wastage and minimizing the effect of form obsolescence. Many high-speed impact printers print in general on approximately 11×14 in. paper. The paper savings by printing on 8.5×11 in. paper, as is possible with any of the laser printers discussed, reduces paper costs by 40% based on reduced paper area. The fixed fonts of impact printers limit document complexity and minimum size. We can summarize our printer system discussion by saying that the end user is motivated by lower cost, increased reliability, increased quality and flexibility, and reduced job completion time. The ability of the high-speed laser nonimpact printer to address these needs is already well proven. Printer specifications are not necessarily a solid indication of which printer will perform best in a specific application. Careful benchmark testing is necessary to arrive at a factual understanding of printer performance capabilities.

X. High-Speed Printer Summary

As we close this discussion, we should briefly look at what our hypothetical high-speed printer running at 400 bits/in. demands in light of current technology and observe what the future may require of our laser-printer technology. One must, of course, make a few speculative remarks, but in general, we can calculate the basic parameters such a system would possess barring "breakthroughs."

In an earlier section, a laser xerographic printer was imagined having 400 resolution elements/in. and running at 4 pages/sec (35 in./sec photo receptor speed). This generated a minimum bandwidth of approximately 62 Mbits/sec. With polygon duty cycles and other system corrections considered the actual bandwidth would probably be closer to 70 Mbits/sec. This is ~3.5 times the bandwidth of the 9700 and ~4.5 times the 3800 bandwidth. The bit time of ~14 nsec is indeed very short. Current electronics are certainly capable of generating data at this rate, but at what complexity and reliability? If, for example, two current printers can do the job of a single hybrid unit and at less cost, why not use multiple printers? The increased image quality allowed by 400-bit/in. printer resolution should certainly be sufficient for very demanding imaging requirements. Are on-line digital pictures required, however? What will be required of graphics?

Generating digital images, whether text or pictures or both, while allowing only $\frac{1}{4}$ sec/image, presents quite a challenge to the electronic-image generation system, let alone the printer. It seems apparent at this jucture in system development that the printer hardware capabilities exceed the image-generation hardware capabilities. This may not be so for long, as continued miniaturization of electronic circuitry continues. Thus, considering polygon rotational velocity practicalities of ~50,000 rpm, modulator bandwidth limits of ~100 Mbits/sec, and xerographic system performance limits of ~40 in./sec, significant printer performance increases are possible. One can probably double both the speed and resolution of current devices before running into difficult engineering limits. Calculated device design parameters, as referenced in the literature, clearly indicate that current printers are not at their limits by a wide margin.

Much technology is market driven, and the current computer printer market does not yet demand the kind of printer performance our technology can provide. This will surely change, however, as more printing is done by computer. Currently, many technologies are used for high-speed printing ranging from impact and ink jet to electrographic, such as the Honeywell PPS system. The highest quality levels, however, are currently achieved by laser xerographic units. Even though very slow by our printer standards, the Xerox Corporation recently introduced a version of its 6500 Color Copier, designated the 6500 CGP, that prints digital color information including pictures. High-speed printers having other than black-and-white capability could all but eliminate the forms market and provide a much-increased use of color in everyday business documents.

The high-speed laser printer has a bright future for the preparation and delivery of hard copy information at impressive quality and speed. The use of laser-printer technology for electronic mail generation around the world is just beginning. Satellite networks for distribution of high-bandwidth data and video are already being developed by various organizations such as Satellite Business Systems (SBS). Recently, AM International (previously called Addressograph-Multigraph, Inc.) anounced the development of a laser-based printer running at 60 images/min. This printer is being developed under contract to SBS. The energy crisis will continue to demand, among other things, more efficient distribution of information. The high-speed laser printer with its associated electronic-image generation capabilities clearly demonstrates its ability to play an important role in current and future information systems.

The author hopes that this discussion has provided the reader, especially the newcomer to laser printing, with a brief look at the technology available. The intent has been to inform the reader on current technology, not to provide a detailed design guide. Design details can be found in many of the references cited.

References

Alphonse, G. A. (1972). Broad-band acoustooptic deflectors using sonic gratings for first order beam steering, *RCA Review,* **33,** 543.

Bayer, B. E. (1973). An optimum method for two-level rendition of continuous-tone pictures, *IEEE Int. Conf. Commun.* **1,** 11.

Born, M., and Wolf, E. (1964). "Principles of Optics," 2nd ed. Pergamon Press, New York.

Born, M., and Wolf, E. (1966). "Principles of Optics," 3rd. ed. Pergamon, New York.

Boyd, J. R., Young, E. H., and Yao, S. K. (1977). Design procedure for wide bandwidth acoustooptic modulator, *Opt. Eng.* **16** (5), 452.

Bracale, M., and Lombardi, A. (1970). The design of broadband light modulators, *Radio Electron. Eng.* **39** (4), 185.

Brosens, P. J. (1971). "Fast Retrace Optical Scanning," *Electro-Optical Systems Design.*

Buzzard, R. J. (1976). Gas lasers for information handling—A review,"
   Opt. Eng. **15** (2), 77.

Calligaris, F., Ciuti, P., and Gabrielli, I. (1973). Extended theory of
   light modulation in thin-screen diffraction by ultrasound, *J. Opt.
   Soc. Am.* **63** (3), 287.

Chen, I. (1978). Electrophotographic characteristics of overcoated photoreceptors, *Photo. Sci. Eng.* **22** (3), 168.

Claus, C. J. (1969). Electrophotographic processes and materials,
   Image Technol., April/May.

Coherent Associates, 42 Shelter Rock Road, Danbury, Connecticut.

Coquin, G. A., Griffin, J. P., and Anderson, L. K. (1970). Wide-band
   acoustooptic deflectors using acoustic beam steering. *IEEE Trans.
   Sonics Ultrasonics* **SU-17** (1), 34.

Crews, R. W., and Rice, P. (1961). The videograph tube—A new component for high speed printing, *IRE Trans. Electron Devices* **ED-
   8**.

Cunniff, J. C. (1973). Scanning with integrated optics, *Opt. Eng.* **12**
   (2), 70.

Debye, P., and Sears, F. W. (1932.) *Proc. Nat. Acad. Sci. U. S. A.*
   18, 410.

Dickson, L. D. (1972). Optical considerations for an acoustooptic deflector, *Appl. Opt.* **11** (10), 2196.

Dunn, M. H., and Ross, J. N. (1976). The argon ion laser, *Progr. Quan-
   tum Electron.* **4**.

Ellis, B., and Walton, A. K. (1971). A bibliography on optical modulators, *in* "Infrared Physics," Vol. 11, p. 85. Pergamon Press,
   New York.

Fleischer, J. M., Latta, M. R., and Rabedeau, M. E. (1977). Laser
   optical system of the IBM 3800 printer, *IBM J. Res. Dev.* **21**, 480.

Foster, L. C., Crumly, C. B., and Cohoon, R. L. (1970). A high-resolution linear optical scanner using a traveling-wave acoustic lens,
   Appl. Opt. **9** (9),

Goldstein, R. (1968). Pockels cell primer, *Laser Focus,* Feb.

Hance, H. V., and Parks, J. K. (1965). Measurement of light-sound
   interaction efficiencies in solids, *J. Acoust. Soc. Am.* **38**, 14.

Johnson, R. V. (1977). Temporal response of the acoustooptic modulator, *Appl. Opt.* **16** (2), 507.

Korpel, A., Adler, R., Desmares, P., and Watson, W. (1966). A television display using acoustic deflection and modulation of light, *Proc. IEEE* **54**, 1429.

Kuchenbecker, H., and Unger, H. (1977). "The New Laser Printer from Siemens," Siemens Aktiengesellschaft, Data Report V (1977), No. 1, pp 4–9.

Lucero, J. A., Duardo, J. A., and Johnson, R. V. (1976). The effect of laser beam transverse mode and polarization properties on A-O modulator performance, *SPIE, Acousto-Optics* **90**, 32.

Meimel, R. F. (1950). "Mechanics of the Gyroscope." Dover, New York.

Meye, W. (1977). Optical character generation for a high-speed non-impact printer, *J. Photogr. Sci.* **25**, 183.

Michalec, G. W. (1966). "Precision Gearing Theory and Practice," Wiley, New York.

Moore, A. D. (1972). Electrostatics, *Sci. Am.,* **47**.

Pockels, F. (1893). *Abhandl., Gesell., Göttingen* **39** (1).

Polky, J. N., and Harris, J. N. (1972). Interdigital electrooptic thin-film modulator, *Appl. Phys. Lett.* **21** (7).

Raman, C. V., and Nath, N. S. N. (1935). *Proc Ind. Acad. Sci.* **A2**, 406: **2**, 413 (1935); **3**, 75 (1936); **3**, 119 (1936); **3**, 459 (1936).

Roetling, P. G. (1977a). Analysis of detail and spurious signals in half-tone images, *J. Appl. Photogr. Eng.* **3** (1), 12.

Roetling, P. G. (1977b). Binary approximation of continuous tone images, *Photogr. Sci. Eng.* **21** (2), 60.

Schlichting, H. (1968). "Boundary Layer Theory," 6th ed. McGraw–Hill, New York.

Vahtra, U., and Wolter, R. F. (1978). *IBM J. Res. Dev.* **22** (1), 2.

White, G. (1971). Optical modulation at high information rates, *Bell Syst. Tech. J.* **50** (8), 2607.

Wolter, R. F. (1978). *J. Appl. Photogr. Eng.* **4** (4), 151.

Zook, J. D. (1974). Light beam deflector performance: A comparitive analysis, *Appl. Opt.* **13** (4), 875.

AUTHOR INDEX

Numbers in italics refer to the pages on which the complete references are listed.

SUBJECT INDEX

A

Acoustooptic cell-driver diagram, 144
Acoustooptic deflectors, 148–153
Acoustooptic materials, selection of, 140
Acoustooptic modulation, in high-speed
   laser printing systems, 139–145
Aerodynamic stabilizer, in video-disc
   systems, 89
AM International, 187
Amplitude measurement, ESPI in, 51
Argon-ion laser, 131–132

B

Bissel function fringes, 36
   see also Fringe analysis; Young's
   fringe pattern
Bit, defined, 128
Boundary Layer Theory (Schlichting),
   160

C

Charge-coupled devices, in video-disc
   tangential correction, 112
Closed-circuit television, in electronic
   speckle pattern interferometry, 45
Color television
   color endoding in, 78–79
   phase and hue in, 79–80
Columbia Broadcasting System EVR
   player, 90
Continuous-wave laser, high-speed image
   recording and, 125–126

D

Deflectors
   acoustooptic, 148–153
   electrooptic, 147–148
   in high-speed laser printing systems,
   145–153
Diode lasers, in video-disc systems,
   116–118
Displacement measurement, ESPI and,
   48
Dual-beam speckle interferometry
   for out-of-plane displacement
   measurement, 23–24
   schematic diagram of, 22
Dual speckle-field interferometry, 20–25
Dual-wavelength ESPI, 54–56, *see also*
   Electronic speckle pattern
   interferometry
   schematic diagram of, 54

E

Electronic speckle pattern
   interferometry, 4, 45–56
   in amplitude measurement, 51
   applications of, 47–48
   block diagram of, 46–47
   commercial availability of, 62
   displacement measurement and, 48
   dual-wavelength, 54–56
   experimental techniques with, 47
   scan converter memories in, 50–51
   time-averaged vibration mode in, 50
   tympanic membrane recordings with,
   52
   vibration analysis and, 48–54